Letts

C000148084

SUCCESS FOR SCHOOLS

1

KS3 FRAMEWORK COURSE

SCIENCE

LEVELS 4–7

CONTENTS

2

UNIT 7 PARTICLE MODEL OF SOLIDS, LIQUIDS AND GASES

UNIT 8 SOLUTIONS

UNIT 9 ENERGY RESOURCES

UNIT 10 ELECTRICAL CIRCUITS

UNIT 11 FORCES AND THEIR EFFECTS

UNIT 12 THE SOLAR SYSTEM AND BEYOND

REVIEWING YEAR 6

Cells

Living things

1 Which of these things are alive?

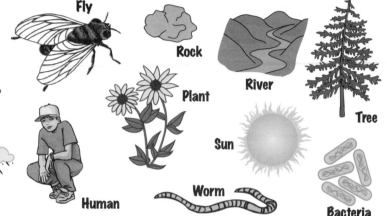

Figure 1 **Alive or not?**

This is MRS GREN

She will help you to remember that **all** living things have these 7 characteristics:

Movement	Get bigger and change
Respiration	Get rid of waste
Sensitivity	Feed
Growth	Breathe
Reproduction	Produce young
Excretion	Change position
Nutrition	Feel and notice things

2 Match the words to their correct meaning.

Moving the body

When you lift the weight, your muscles pull the bones in your arm. Your muscles use up lots of oxygen when you exercise.

3 Can you remember how the oxygen travels to your muscles? Hint: See Figure 3.

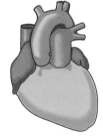

Figure 3

Figure 2 **Arm bones and muscles**

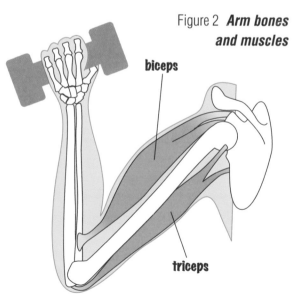

biceps

triceps

Cells

There's something else all living things have in common – they are all made of **cells**.

Interdependence

Habitats

4 Look at the pictures in Figure 4.

- Match the animal to its correct habitat.
- Choose one of the animals and explain how it is adapted to the area where it lives.

Figure 4 **Animals and habitats**

Food chains

5 Put these words in the correct order to show the direction of energy flow in a food chain:

TOP CARNIVORE   **PRIMARY CONSUMER**

SUN   **PLANT**

Classification keys

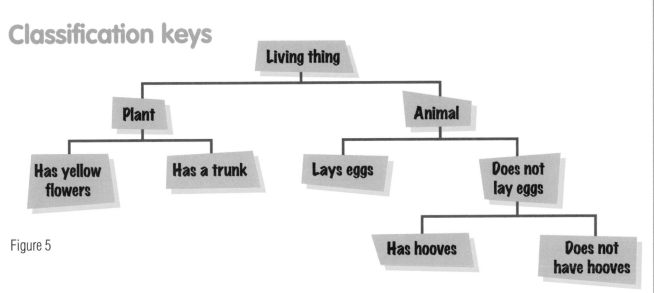

Figure 5

6 Use the key to position these living things correctly:

Figure 6

REVIEWING YEAR 6

Solids, liquids and gases

States of matter

Figure 1 *Substances in the kitchen*

1 In Figure 1, find:

a some solids that dissolve in water

b a solid that melts easily

c an example of a reversible change and of an irreversible change

d two liquids

e a mixture

f an example of evaporation happening

g an example of condensation happening.

Reversible changes of state

ice (a solid)   **water (a liquid)**   **steam (a gas)**

 m_____ 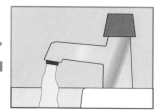 e_____

f_____ c_____

Figure 2 *Changing state*

2

a Copy and complete the sentence.
When a solid (e.g. ice) m_____, it turns into a liquid (e.g. water).

b Write three more sentences for the other changes in the diagram.

3 What is the reversible change in the drawing? How would you reverse the change?

Don't worry, mum, it's a reversible change.

Dissolving and separating

Dissolve or not?

The diagrams show what happens when four substances are mixed with water.

Figure 3

4 Which of the substances in Figure 3 **dissolve** in water?
Which substances **do not dissolve**? How can you tell?

Separating

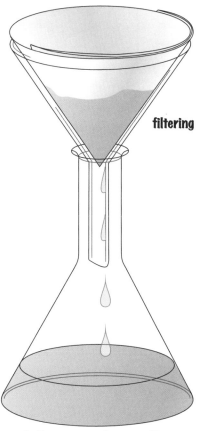

Figure 4 *Two ways of separating*

5 Choose which separating equipment –
filtering or evaporating – would get each
solid in Figure 3 back out of the water.

a Copper sulphate

b Chalk

c Sand

d Salt

REVIEWING YEAR 6

Electricity | Things used in circuits

The names of some items used in electric circuits are listed on the left.

1 Copy the list and match each item to the letter for its correct description.

cell	**A**	source of electricity
conductor	**B**	gives out light when electricity passes in it
insulator	**C**	is used to turn electricity on and off
lamp	**D**	allows electricity to pass through it easily
motor	**E**	spins when electricity passes in it
switch	**F**	does not allow electricity to pass through it

2 Draw the circuit symbols for a cell, a lamp, a motor and a switch.

3 Copy the table and classify each material as a conductor or an insulator by placing a tick in the correct column.

  a Which type of materials are the best conductors of electricity?

  b Which are the worst?

Material	Conductor	Insulator
brass		
copper		
iron		
plastic		
wood		

4 In the circuits of Figure 1, all the lamps are the same.

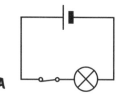 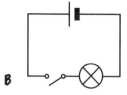 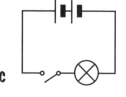 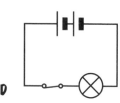

Figure 1   A   B   C   D

  a Which circuit has the brightest lamp?   **b** Why is this lamp the brightest?

Seeing

Most objects are either **sources** of light, or **reflectors** of light, or **detectors** of light.

5 Brainstorm to produce a list of up to six of each type of object.

6 Use diagrams to explain how:

  a only two of these objects are needed to watch television

  b three of these objects are needed to look at a tree.

7 Copy and complete Figure 2 to show the effects that different types of surface have on light. Does each one **reflect** or **absorb** light?

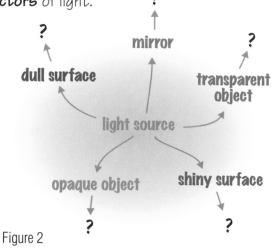

Figure 2

Shadows

8 Use the best words from the list to complete the sentences.

block   curved   opaque   straight   transmit   transparent

Shadows are formed because light travels in _____ lines and does not travel through _____ objects. These objects _____ light.

9 Figure 3 shows how a shadow picture is made on a screen.

a Explain why it is better to use a white screen than a black screen.

b State *one* way in which the hand and its shadow are similar.

c State *two* ways in which the hand and its shadow are different.

d State *two* ways in which the size of the shadow can be made bigger.

e Draw a diagram to show where a person needs to be in order to see the shadow.

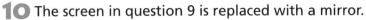

Figure 3

screen

hand

bright light

10 The screen in question 9 is replaced with a mirror.

a Can a person standing anywhere in front of the mirror see his or her reflection? Where does he or she have to be?

b Describe *three* differences between the reflection seen in a mirror and the shadow seen on a screen.

c If you look at the surface of a pond, you can see shadows and also reflections. A friend asks, 'How can I tell the difference between a shadow and a reflection?' State one *key* difference that would enable your friend to tell the difference.

Forces

11 Starting with 'Forces', draw a mind map on the classroom board that includes:
- what forces do
- how forces are shown on diagrams
- how forces are measured
- how forces are described.

12 Write a description of each force shown in Figure 4. Your description should include:
- the object that is exerting the force
- whether the force is a push or a pull
- the object that is being pushed or pulled.

Figure 4

Moon

13 How many forces are acting on the plasticine in Figure 5? Write a description of each force.

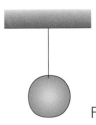

Figure 5

INTRODUCTION TO YEAR 7 KEY IDEAS
Cells

Starter

- As a class, brainstorm everything that the word 'cell' means to you.
- Highlight the ideas that you think are connected to Science.
- Use a dictionary to look up the word 'cell'.
- At the end of the topic on Cells, your class can return to the brainstorm and see how much you have learnt since then.

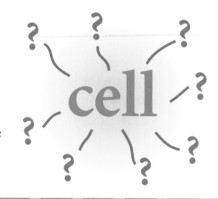

Building on what you have learnt

- Cells are known as the 'building blocks of life'.
- You have already learnt that living things feed and grow, and that plants make their own food by **photosynthesis**.
- At Key Stage 3, you will learn that cells make these things happen.

1 Work in pairs with a 2-minute time limit. Write down 5 facts about feeding and growing.

- In Year 7, you will look at cells through a microscope as well as in pictures.
- If you make a model it will help you to remember that a cell is a three-dimensional structure.
- Cells from plants are not quite the same as cells from animals. You will need to learn what they have in common and the differences between them.

Figure 2 is a picture of bacteria. Each one is a single cell. Some bacteria are useful but others are harmful.

2 Give one example of how bacteria can be useful and one of how they can be harmful.

- In Year 7 you will learn that many plants and animals are actually made out of millions of different types of cells.
- The cells have to be organised to form the body of a living thing. You will learn how they group together.

3 In groups, list the names of as many organs in the human body as you can think of, and then compare your list with another group.

Figure 1 *There are differences between cells in plants and cells in animals*

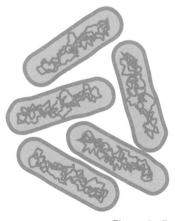

Figure 2 *Bacteria*

- Cells are also important for making babies.
- In Year 7 you will learn how human babies are made and why everyone is individual and unique.
- Seeds are 'baby' plants.
- To make a seed, two cells need to join together.

4 Which part of the plant makes the seeds?

5 Name the flower parts in Figure 3.

6 Fill in the missing words below:

_____ + _____ = seed

What is the joining together called?

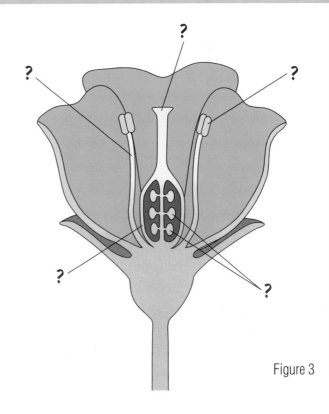

Figure 3

Figure 4 **Ways that seeds are spread**

Some seeds are specially adapted to grip onto fur and feathers

Some seeds such as blackberry pips and rose hips are spread by animals, including birds, when they eat the fruits

Some seeds travel by water

Some seeds blow on the wind

The seed pods of the Himalayan balsam explode to scatter the seeds

INTRODUCTION TO YEAR 7 KEY IDEAS
Interdependence

Starter

- Look up the word 'interdependence' in the dictionary.
  It might seem a difficult idea to understand, but you have actually done a lot of work about this already.

Building on what you have learnt

1 Draw a food chain of your own.

- Each living thing in the chain depends on the one before it for energy.
- All living things depend on the Sun.
- This is **interdependence**.

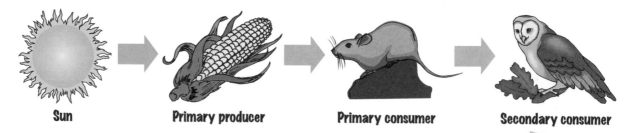

Sun   Primary producer   Primary consumer   Secondary consumer

Transfer of energy

Figure 1 *A food chain*

2 Look at the food chain in Figure 1.

- Which animal is the top carnivore?

- What would happen to the animals if we took the plants away?

- In Year 7 you will extend your work on food chains to look at food webs and populations.
- There is a balance between the plants and animals living together in a habitat.
- Living things have to compete with each other if they are going to survive.
- Only those that are best adapted manage to feed and breed successfully.

Figure 2 *Levels in food chains and webs*

- Living things also need water to survive.

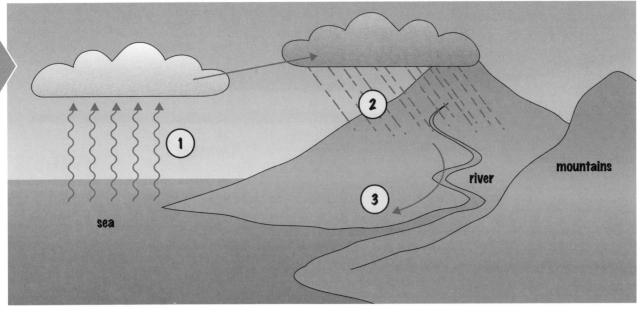

Figure 3 *The water cycle*

3 Look at Figure 3 and explain what is happening at each numbered stage.

- In Year 7 you will learn that the offspring of all living things are individual and unique.
- This **variation** is important if living things are going to adapt to the changes in the environment.

As soot built up in towns, the variation in the peppered moth helped it to survive. The moths are either a creamy-white colour or a dark grey. The dark grey ones survive better in towns because they are camouflaged from predators.

Figure 4 *Peppered moths, camouflaged and visible*

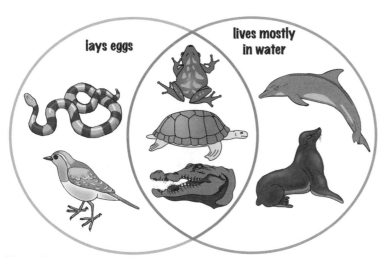

Figure 5

- There are so many living things on planet Earth that it helps to put them into groups.
- In Year 7 you will learn how scientists group living things, and the reasons why certain **species** are put together.

INTRODUCTION TO YEAR 7 KEY IDEAS

Particles

Starter

Sort these substances into **solids**, **liquids** and **gases**.
- How can you tell if a substance is a solid?
- How can you tell if a substance is a liquid?
- How can you tell if a substance is a gas?

wood　　**milk**

air

glass　　**petrol**

Building on what you have learnt

Solids, liquids and gases

Solids
- **Are** hard
- **Cannot be** squashed
- **Cannot** change shape

Liquids
- **Can be** poured
- **Are the** same shape as their container

Gases
- **Can be** any shape
- **Can be** squashed easily
- **Are** very light

Figure 1

1 In groups, look at this list. These substances are more difficult to classify as solids, liquids or gases.

paper clip　　**jelly**　　**treacle**　　**bowl of dried peas**

plasticine　　**bath sponge**　　**flour**

Discuss each substance in your group. Use sentences like these to start your discussion about each substance: 'I think it is a …' 'The reason it doesn't fit exactly is because …'

14

Explaining changes

In Year 7 you will learn that many changes you see in the world around you can be explained by using **scientific ideas** about things you cannot see. All the changes in Figure 2 can be explained by using ideas about **gases**.

Snowmen disappear when the weather gets warmer

When wood burns it leaves very little waste behind

Petrol seems to disappear during long journeys

Lemonade gets lighter when it goes flat

Figure 2 **Changes**

2 Work as a group to discuss the reasons for what you see in each diagram. In pairs, draw a diagram with 'explanation bubbles' to describe what you think is happening in one of the examples. Present your ideas to other groups.

Figure 3

Acids and safety

⚠ You will be learning about acids and how to carry out hazardous experiments safely.

Some acids that you will be using are **corrosive** – they can damage your skin and eyes. Some acids that you will be learning about are so safe that you can eat or drink them! But when you are using 'food acids' at school you should never taste them.

This lab acid is corrosive

Hydrochloric Acid

CORROSIVE

Acids are in our foods

Vinegar

3 Discuss in groups why it could be dangerous to taste a substance in the lab, even if it is an everyday food. As a class, write your ideas on the board and discuss them.

wide sleeves

long hair

safety specs

open toed shoes

shoes with closed toes

sitting down on a stool

Figure 4

Safe or not?

When working with corrosive acids you will need to think about how to make sure you *do not knock things over*. You will also need to think about how to make sure you are *safe* if an acid spill happens.

4 Work in pairs.

a Which *two* of these pictures show ways of keeping safe? Discuss your reasons.

b What could go wrong in the other pictures? Draw a cartoon strip to show how an acid accident can happen.

5 Look around your lab. In what ways is a lab different from a normal classroom? How does the design of the lab help keep you safe during practical work?

Forces

Starter

What happens when a heavy and lighter iron ball are let go at the same time from the top of the Leaning Tower of Pisa?

- Galileo said that they would fall together.

- His critics said that the heavier ball would fall faster.

Who do you think was right?
As a class, write down your ideas and reasons on the classroom board.

Building on what you have learnt

What forces do

Darren is thinking about forces. He lines up his catapult to a conker. He knows that forces can make things:

- change shape
- change speed
- change direction.

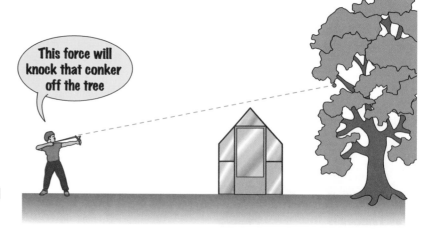

This force will knock that conker off the tree

Figure 1

1 Copy the table. For each line, place a tick in one or more columns to describe the effect of the force.

Force	Change of speed	Change of shape	Change of direction
Darren pulls the elastic			
The elastic pushes the stone			
The Earth pulls the stone			
The air pushes the stone			

2 As usual, Darren misses.
What do you think is likely to happen when the stone is released from the catapult? Draw this on a diagram based on Figure 1.

Combining forces

Forces can act together on the same object.

3 Working in pairs, use two forcemeters and a wooden block to find the effect of the pairs of forces shown in Figure 2. Record your results in a table.
In which diagram does the block act as if there were no forces acting on it at all?

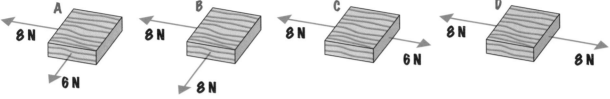

Figure 2

Planets in the Solar System

Figure 3 *The Solar System*

4 Which is the biggest planet in the Solar System? Which is the smallest?
The table shows the diameter of each planet compared to the Earth.
List the planets in order of physical size.

Planet:	Mercury	Venus	Earth	Mars	Jupiter	Saturn	Uranus	Neptune	Pluto
Diameter (Earth = 1.0)	0.38	0.95	1.0	0.53	11	9.5	4.0	2.1	0.08

5 Make a model of the planets in the Solar System.
Colour each planet to show its appearance from space.
Place them in the correct order from the Sun.
Explain why you cannot make a *scale* model of the planets with their orbits.

The Sun and time

Before there were clocks, people told the time of day by the movement of the Sun across the sky, using a **sundial**.

6 In pairs, use a lamp as a model Sun and a piece of plasticine sticking up on a sheet of white paper as a model sundial.
- Model the movement of the Sun across the sky in summer.
- Trace the movement of the shadow across the paper.
- Do the same for autumn and winter.

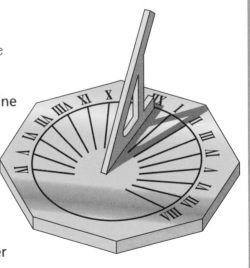

Explain how your model sundial shows that:

a the Sun rises higher in the sky in autumn than in winter

b days are longer in summer than in autumn.

7 In which season is the Sun's shadow similar to that in spring?

INTRODUCTION TO YEAR 7 KEY IDEAS
Energy

Starter

As a class, think of the ways in which each item has energy and how it can be used. For each object shown, make a list on the class board.

coal

Building on what you have learnt

Generating electricity

Most UK power stations generate their electricity using the energy from burning fuels such as coal and gas. Small amounts of electricity are generated from sources such as the wind and moving water, and a larger amount is generated from nuclear power.

A new power station is to be built close to a village, and there is some debate about the type of power station that is planned. Figure 1 shows two groups of protesters.

Figure 1

1 As a class, divide into two groups. One group prepares and gives a presentation, putting forward the arguments in favour of nuclear power. The other group argues the opposite case.
Each group can produce a wall display to spread their message to the rest of the school.

Energy transfer

Electricity is used at home to produce **heat, movement** and **light**.

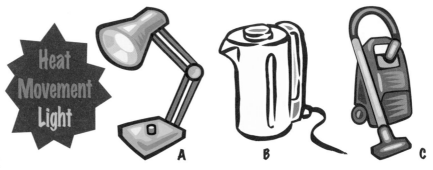

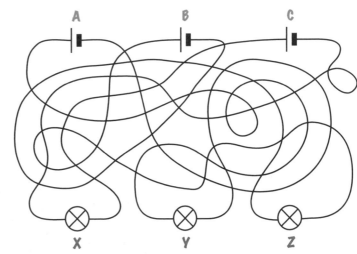

Figure 2

2 Write down the types of energy listed in Figure 2 and, alongside each, write the letter for the device that is best at producing it.

An electrical puzzle

Figure 3 shows a complex arrangement of cells, bulbs and wires.
None of the wires join where they cross.

3 Work out which bulb is joined to each cell.

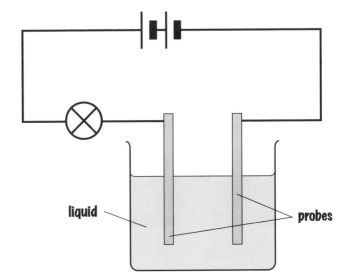

Figure 3

Electrical conductors

Metals conduct electricity, and all other materials are insulators.

4 Work in pairs to decide whether the statement above is true or false. Give your reasons.

5 Use a circuit like the one in Figure 4 to test a number of liquids.

Figure 4

liquid

probes

Use a table like the one below to record:
• what happens in the liquid
• the brightness of the bulb.
Explain what your observations show about whether liquids can conduct electricity.

Liquid	Observations of liquid	Brightness of bulb

CELL STRUCTURE

AIMS

By the end of this section you should:
• **Understand what a cell is.**
• **Be able to label a diagram of a cell.**
• **Know the differences between plant and animal cells.**

STARTER

All living things (<u>organisms</u>) are made from <u>cells</u>. That is why cells are known as 'the building blocks of life'. In groups, brainstorm for 5 minutes to list as many different organisms as you can think of. Count up how many the class thought of and consider that they all are made from cells.

CELLS AND ORGANISMS

Figure 1

All of these are organisms.
• Some organisms have only one cell.
• Other <u>multi-celled organisms</u> are made from millions of cells that are working together.

THE DIFFERENCES BETWEEN ANIMAL CELLS AND PLANT CELLS

Only plant cells have:	Because:
• a **cell wall** made of cellulose	• it provides extra strength and support so that the plant can stand upright.
• a **vacuole** containing cell sap (a solution of sugar and salts)	• it helps the plant cell to keep its shape.
• <u>chloroplasts</u> containing the green pigment chlorophyll	• they absorb sunlight energy so the plant can make its own food by <u>photosynthesis</u>.

LOOKING AT CELLS

- Cells are very small so we need to use a <u>microscope</u> to see them clearly.
- Things appear larger when you look at them through a microscope. You can calculate the <u>magnification</u>.

Activity

1 Make a slide of your own cheek cells. ⚠ Use a new cotton bud and dispose of it safely. You need to stain the cells with a dye to show up the different parts.

Figure 2 *Cheek cell from an animal*

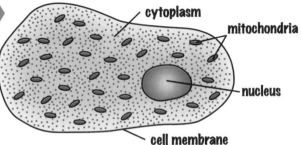

cytoplasm, mitochondria, nucleus, cell membrane

Figure 3 *Leaf cell from a plant*

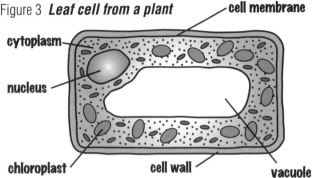

cell membrane, cytoplasm, nucleus, chloroplast, cell wall, vacuole

Both the animal and plant cells have:	Because:
• a <u>nucleus</u>	• it is the control centre of the cell; • the genes (instructions) are in here.
• cytoplasm	• all the chemical reactions of the cell take place in this jelly-like liquid, to keep the organism alive.
• cell membrane	• it holds the cell together and controls the substances that pass in and out of the cell.

∞ *Links to other key ideas*
Think about the links with Reproduction (pages 30 to 33).

Activity

2 In groups, make your own 3D model of a cell. Think about the materials you could use to represent the different parts.

Activity

3 In pairs, prepare a microscope slide of onion cells. Look at the onion cells and compare them with the plant cell above.
(a) What are missing from the onion cells?
(b) Why are they not found in onion cells?

REVIEW

4 Take a piece of paper or a whiteboard. On one side, write 'Both plant and animal cells'. On the other side write 'Plant cells only'. Your teacher will read out the names of parts of a cell. Hold up the paper or whiteboard with the correct side towards the teacher.

5 Quick-fire quiz: In groups, take 5 minutes to prepare brief answers to the following questions. Your teacher will write down three answers to each question and ask the class to discuss which is the best and why.
(a) What is an organism?
(b) What does 'multi-celled' mean?
(c) What three things do both plant and animal cells have?
(d) What is the function of: the nucleus; the cell membrane?
(e) What three things do only plant cells have?

6 Write a story describing what it would be like to go inside a plant cell.

Follow the mouse
www.biology4kids.com
www.bbc.co.uk/bites

SPECIALISED CELLS

AIMS

By the end of this section you should:
- **Know that multi-celled organisms consist of specialised cells.**
- **Be able to name some specialised cells.**
- **Explain how the structure of a specialised cell helps it to function.**

STARTER

Multi-celled organisms have different parts to their bodies. In humans, parts include the brain, eyes, bones, lungs. Each part does its own particular job to keep the body alive. Each part of the body is made from special types of cell, and these cells have a structure that helps them to carry out their functions.

- In pairs or small groups, think of 5 different types of cell in the human body. If this is too easy, choose another organism. You have a 2-minute time limit.

SPECIALISED PLANT CELLS

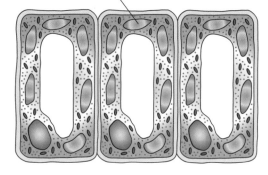

chloroplast

Figure 7 *Palisade cells*

In the palisade cells of the leaf there are lots of chloroplasts. These cells are near the top surface so that the light reaches the chloroplasts for photosynthesis.

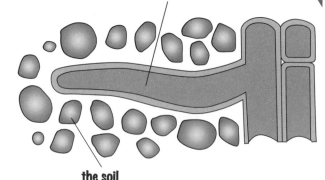

root hair

the soil

Figure 8 *A root hair cell*

Root hair cells are long and thin. Their shape makes the surface area large so that they can absorb a lot of water and minerals from the soil.

Activity

2 View a prepared slide of a specialised cell.
- Do a labelled drawing and swap with other pupils to guess which cell it is.
- Explain how you recognised the one you were given.

Follow the mouse

www.biology4kids.com
www.auscape.com.au
http//wwwvet.murdoch.edu.au/spermatology
www.scripps.edu/pub/goodsell/rbc/rbc
www.learn.co.uk

SPECIALISED ANIMAL CELLS

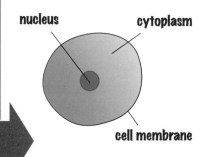

Figure 1 *An ovum (egg cell)*

Ova (egg cells) have a nucleus containing **chromosomes** (genes) from the mother. The cytoplasm is yolky so that it can be used for food if the ovum is **fertilised**. This makes the ovum much larger than a sperm cell.

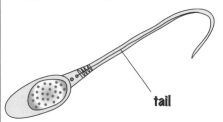

Figure 2 *A sperm cell*

A **sperm** cell has a nucleus containing chromosomes from the father. The **tail** moves so that the sperm cell can swim to meet the ovum. The head can break through the wall of the ovum.

⚭ *Links to other key ideas*

Think about the links with Reproduction (pages 30–33).

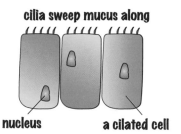

Figure 3 *Ciliated cells in airway*

Ciliated cells line the airways into your **lungs**. They produce **mucus** to stick to dust and **bacteria**, and so stop them entering your lungs. The cilia are hairs that brush the mucus up into the throat where you swallow it.

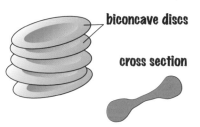

Figure 4 *The shape of red blood cells*

Red blood cells have no nucleus. They have a large **surface area**. This gives them more space to carry **oxygen** around the body.

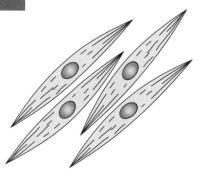

Figure 5 *Muscle cells*

Muscle cells are stretched so that they can shorten and make the muscle **contract**. When muscles contract, they make parts of the body move.

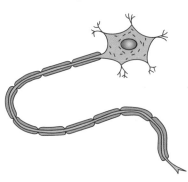

Figure 6 *A nerve cell*

Nerve cells need to conduct electrical signals around the body. Their shape, like wires, allows this to happen.

WS 2

Activity

1 Read through the information about specialised plant and animal cells until you are sure you understand it. Then close the book and try to match the pictures of the cells to their correct descriptions on the worksheet.

REVIEW

3 'Fist of five': Your teacher will show you some pictures of specialised cells to identify, and will ask questions about the structure and function of each cell. If you are certain you know the answer, show all 5 fingers, otherwise hold up the number of fingers that show how sure you are.

4 Choose one specialised cell from this section. Explain how the cell membrane, cytoplasm and nucleus are adapted, and why.

STRUCTURE OF ORGANISMS

AIMS
By the end of this section you should:
- **Understand how cells group together to form organ systems.**
- **Appreciate how scientific discovery has developed our understanding of the structure of organisms.**

HUMAN ORGAN SYSTEMS

There are 9 <u>organ systems</u> in the body.
- The skeletal system ⎱ together these make the body move
- The muscle system ⎰
- The respiratory system: for breathing and getting energy from food
- The <u>digestive system</u>: to break down food
- The <u>circulatory system</u> = blood as a transport system
- The <u>reproductive system</u>
- The <u>nervous system</u>: to send messages around the body quickly
- The endocrine system: to send messages around the body slowly
- The excretory system: to get rid of waste that can be poisonous

Activity
1 Use the card organs from the Starter activity. Divide the cards into groups to match the systems in the list on the left.

Follow the mouse
www.ucmp.berkeley.edu/history/hooke
www.utmem.edu/~thjones/hist/hist_mic
www.denniskunkel.com
www.pbrc.hawaii.edu/bemf/microangela

Activity
3 In pairs, visit websites in the list, and use other sources, to find out how light and electron microscopes were invented and developed. Put the class information together in a time-line display.

SCIENTIFIC DISCOVERY

Scientists discovered that **organisms** consist of organs before they discovered tissues and cells. It was only when the **microscope** was invented that they could see cells. In 1665, Robert Hooke examined a thin slice of cork and saw that it looked like 'a great many little boxes'. He called these boxes cells from the Latin word meaning 'a little room'.

We still use the word cell today, but Hooke was a long way from fully understanding the importance of cells. Microscopes are continually being improved so that we can **magnify** smaller and smaller objects. Scientists can then gain a greater understanding of how things work.

STARTER

Specialised cells group together to form organs.

In small groups, you have 3 minutes to position the organs onto the card model of the human body. For each organ you put in the correct position, your group will gain 1 point.

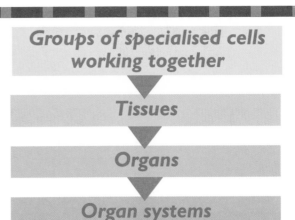

Groups of specialised cells working together

⬇

Tissues

⬇

Organs

⬇

Organ systems

⬇

Organism

PLANT ORGAN SYSTEMS

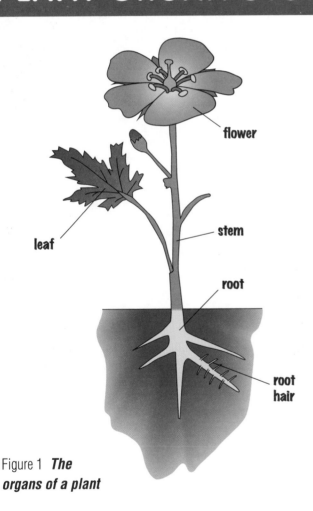

flower

leaf

stem

root

root hair

Figure 1 *The organs of a plant*

Flower: the reproductive organ
Leaf: absorbs light for photosynthesis
Stem: supports the plant and transports substances
Roots: anchor the plant into the ground, and absorb water and minerals from the soil

Activity

2 Look at prepared slides showing the specialised cells that make up plant organ systems.

REVIEW

4 Using the flow chart in the Starter panel, complete Worksheet 3 by providing examples for:
• plants
• a human.

WS 3

GROWTH

AIMS

By the end of this section you should:
- **Understand how an organism grows.**
- **Be able to interpret data and understand the importance of sample size for producing reliable results.**

INTERPRETING DATA

A pollen grain landing on the stigma of a flower grows a pollen tube to reach and fertilise an ovule.

To get pollen tubes to grow in the laboratory, grains were put into sugar solution. 20 grains went into each concentration and were left for a set time. The grains were then viewed under a microscope to count how many had grown tubes.

Concentration of sugar solution	Number of pollen tubes grown
0.2	3
0.4	6
0.6	10
0.8	12
1.0	16

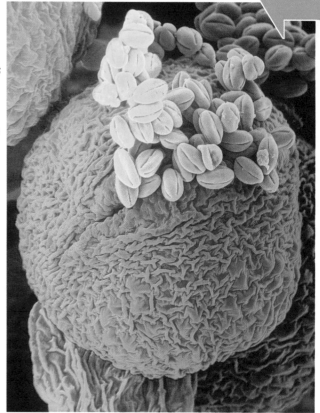

Figure 3 *Pollen grains develop on flower anthers*

Activity

2 Look at the results table.
(a) Draw a line graph of these results.
(b) To explain what the results show, complete this sentence: As the concentration of sugar solution increases, the number of pollen tubes…
(c) What is your conclusion about the growth of pollen tubes?
(d) Why were 20 pollen grains used in each concentration?
(e) How would repeating the experiment help to make the results more reliable?

STARTER

Your teacher will show you the axes of a graph like this:

- Predict the shape of the graph for a growing organism.
- How would the shape differ for faster growth and for slower growth?
- Organisms consist of cells. How does an organism get bigger as it grows?

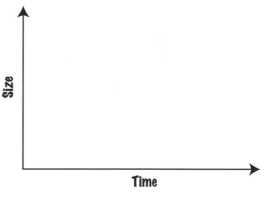

Figure 1 **Graph axes**

GROWTH

For an organism to grow, two things happen:
- The number of cells increases **by cell division**
- The new cells get bigger.

Figure 2 **An animal cell dividing**

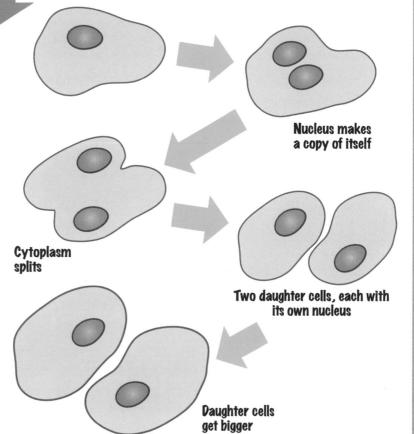

Nucleus makes a copy of itself

Cytoplasm splits

Two daughter cells, each with its own nucleus

Daughter cells get bigger

Activity

1 Use a microscope to view:
- recently divided cells of algae,
- tubes growing from pollen.

REVIEW

3 For each of the following examples, decide if the sample is large enough to produce reliable results and come to a conclusion. Hold up your 'Yes' or 'No' card and be ready to explain your decision.

■ To find out the UK's favourite TV programme, every person in London was sent a questionnaire. When the results were counted, *EastEnders* came top.

■ To find out how much water there is in apples, a scientist crushed one Golden Delicious apple and liquidised it. She separated the liquid out and collected the water which boiled at 100°C. The volume was 15 cm³.

■ While on holiday in Australia, a man wearing red shorts was bitten by a dangerous spider. All tourists are now told not to wear red clothes to avoid being bitten by spiders.

DEVELOPMENT AND PARENTAL CARE

AIMS

By the end of this section you should:
- **Know that organs in the body do not all grow at the same rate.**
- **Be able to relate this to the different levels of care parents give to their offspring.**

HOW NEWBORN ANIMALS SURVIVE

Not all organs grow at the same rate. After birth, the organs of some animals may still need time to develop. During this time, they are cared for by parents.

Follow the mouse
www.bbc.co.uk/reallywild/amazing
www.5tigersorg/Basics
www.earthlife.net/mammals
www.pbs.org/lifeofbirds
www.alienexplorer.com

 WS 5 **Activity**

1. Work in small groups to research one animal using websites.
(a) Find out how the parents care for and protect their young to make sure they survive.
(b) Produce a poster or a PowerPoint presentation to aid your feedback to the rest of the class.

HOW PARENTS CARE FOR THEIR YOUNG

Activity

2. Match up the boxes on the left to the reasons on the right. There may be more than one correct reason for each box.

Birds bring worms to the nest

Calf suckles milk

Hatchling sits on feet of penguin

Joey sits in the pouch of the kangaroo

Eider duck lines nest with feathers

When disturbed, a lapwing flies away from the nest and makes high pitched calls

Bison form a circle with the young in the centre

Killer whales demonstrate to young how to get back into the water from the beach

Chimps remove parasites from each other's fur

Cats lick their kittens' bottoms

Reasons

To keep the young warm

To protect from **predators**

To provide food

To stimulate young to get rid of waste

To teach how to catch **prey**

To teach how to groom

STARTER

- In pairs, take 1 minute to look at the animals below and put them in order, from the one that gets the least <u>parental care</u> to the one that receives the most.

NEWBORN ANIMALS

Figure 1

REVIEW

3 Individually, produce a mind map to summarise everything you have learnt about GROWTH.

4 Revise all of your work on Cells (pages 20–29).

REPRODUCTIVE ORGANS AND CELLS

AIMS

By the end of this section you should:
- **Be able to describe the specialised structure of sperm and egg cells.**
- **Be able to label diagrams of the human male and female reproductive organs.**
- **Explain the differences between the male and female reproductive organs.**

REPRODUCTIVE ORGANS

The sex cells are made and stored in the reproductive organs.
Sperm are produced in the testes, and ova are stored in the ovaries.

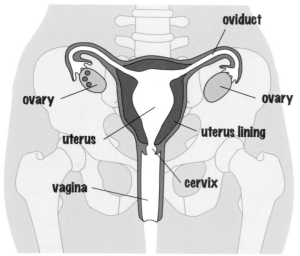

Figure 3 *Female reproductive system*

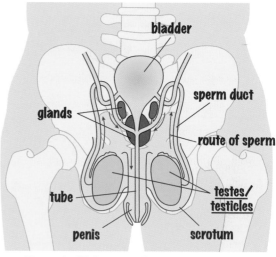

Figure 4 *Male reproductive system*

a Why are the reproductive organs inside the <u>hip bones</u>?

b Why are a woman's hip bones wider than a man's?

c Why do the testes hang outside the body in the scrotum?

d Why do tubes connect the testes to the <u>penis</u>?

e Why is the <u>uterus</u> (womb) made of elastic muscle?

WS 6

Activity

2 Use the diagrams to do the following.
- Check your labels on the worksheet.
- In pairs, discuss the answers to the questions in the box.
- As a class, decide which pair has given the best answer to each question. Think about whether the answer is accurate, clear and concise, and uses the scientific names correctly.

STARTER

- Individually, spend 5 minutes writing freely about everything you know about cells.
- Read through your information and highlight only the sections about cell structure. This might help you to remember more details, so write down anything new you think of.
- Read through again, but this time use a different colour and highlight anything to do with specialised cells.

SEX CELLS

⊙⊙ Links to other key ideas
Think about the links with Specialised cells (page 23).

A baby girl is born with all her eggs (ova) already in two <u>ovaries</u>. When the girl reaches <u>puberty</u>, usually aged 11 or 12, the ova start to mature. One ovum is then released each month as part of the <u>menstrual cycle</u>. When the ovum does not get <u>fertilised</u>, it is lost from the body as a <u>period</u> (menstrual bleeding).

Figure 1 *Female egg cell (ovum)*

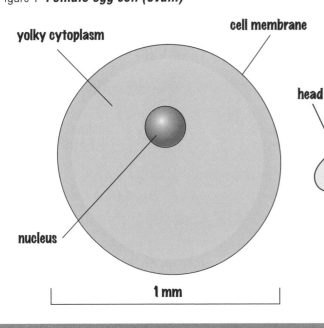

Activity
1 Use photographs, prepared microscope slides or internet pictures to view the three-dimensional structure of the sex cells, and see the difference in size between them.

When a boy reaches puberty, usually aged 12 or 13, the <u>testes</u> start to produce sperm. Boys will start to experience <u>erections</u> and, possibly, <u>wet dreams</u>.

Figure 2 *Male sperm cell*

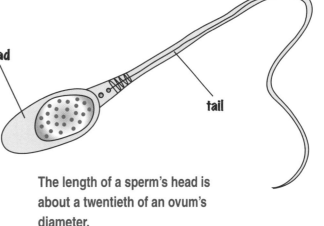

The length of a sperm's head is about a twentieth of an ovum's diameter.

REVIEW

3 Use a whiteboard to draw from memory the male sex cell on one side and the female sex cell on the other. Points will be given for accurate drawings, correct labels and spellings.

4 Revise your Key Stage 2 work on the characteristics of life (see page 4).

Follow the mouse
www.learn.co.uk
www.medem.com
www.mydr.com.au

SEX CELL PRODUCTION AND FERTILISATION

AIMS

By the end of this section you should:
- **Understand many of the changes that happen during** puberty.
- **Be able to describe what happens in the** menstrual cycle.
- **Explain how the** sex cells **are adapted for** fertilisation.

STARTER

Check your knowledge of the scientific terms for this section by solving the anagrams and matching them to the meanings.

ulenusc	female sex cell
vomu	where fertilisation happens
verdicutoper mestys	control centre of the cell
vudicot	organ where ova are stored
aorvy	the part of the body for reproduction

MENSTRUAL CYCLE

Figure 1 *The menstrual cycle*

lining breaks down

lining is building up

uterus lining fully thickened

day 1   day 10   day 14   day 17   day 28

menstrual cycle starts

lining starts to thicken

ovum released from ovary

ovum is travelling to uterus

if fertilised, the ovum will stay in the uterus; if not, the lining breaks down

Day 1–5: **Period.** The unfertilised ovum is lost with the lining of the uterus in a menstrual bleed.

Day 5–14: The bleeding stops and the lining of the uterus starts to thicken again with blood vessels.

Day 14: **Ovulation.** An ovum is released from the ovary and begins travelling through the **oviduct**.

Day 14–28: The uterus lining is ready for a fertilised ovum to be **implanted**. If the ovum is not fertilised, the menstrual cycle begins again.

Remember that the days are approximate because every woman is different. When a girl first starts her periods, it may take time for the cycle to settle into a pattern.

Activity

2 Produce a circular diagram of the menstrual cycle showing what happens on each day. Alternatively, use a calendar to indicate when the period starts, when ovulation takes place and the most likely time for a woman to become **pregnant**.

PUBERTY

Puberty is the first stage in adolescence when the body begins to change from a child to an adult.

Activity

1 Use the problem pages from teenage magazines to see how to write and reply to letters.
Individually, write a letter to an agony aunt. Swap with a partner and reply to each other's letters, offering advice.

	In boys:	In girls:
Hormone controlling changes	Testosterone	Oestrogen and progesterone
Main effect	Testes start to produce sperm.	Ovaries start to release ova (menstrual cycle begins).
Physical changes	Penis grows larger; hair grows on face, chest, under arms and in pubic region; oily skin and hair.	Breasts grow larger; hair grows under arms and in pubic region; hips widen; oily skin and hair.
Emotional changes	Have mood swings; become irritable; become interested in the opposite sex.	

FERTILISATION

Activity

3 Cut out the pictures and labels from the worksheet. Glue them into the correct position on the diagram of the female reproductive organs to show how fertilisation takes place.

- When a man and a woman have sexual intercourse, millions of sperm from the penis are ejaculated into the vagina.
- The sperm cells swim through the uterus and into the oviduct.
- If this happens following ovulation, the sperm have more chance of meeting an ovum.
- Many sperm cells do not reach this far and die along the way but it only needs one sperm to break through the membrane and fertilise the ovum.
- Fertilisation = the fusing together of the nucleus from the sperm cell and the nucleus of the ovum.
- The 2 nuclei contain chromosomes that carry instructions for a new human.
- When the 2 sets of instructions come together at fertilisation, the offspring can develop with characteristics inherited from each parent.
- The child will be similar to both parents, but not identical to either.

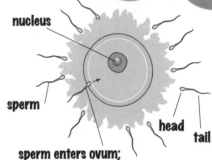

nucleus

sperm

head

tail

sperm enters ovum;
once inside, tail of sperm breaks off
and nucleus in sperm head fuses
with nucleus of ovum

Figure 2 *Fertilisation*

REVIEW

4 Use a whiteboard to draw from memory the male sex cell on one side and the female sex cell on the other. Swap your board with a partner and annotate the labels to explain how the cells are adapted for fertilisation. Think about which parts:

- contain the chromosomes carrying the inherited information from parents
- move the sperm cell
- can break through the membrane of the ovum cell
- contain the food for the ovum cell once fertilised.

5 Learn the spellings and the meanings of the key words for this lesson.

Follow the mouse
www.coolnurse.com
www.keepkidshealthy.com/adolescent/puberty
www.kotex.com/info/education
www.learn.co.uk
www.letsstudy.co.uk/student

INTERNAL AND EXTERNAL FERTILISATION; PREGNANCY

AIMS

By the end of this section you should:
- **Understand the difference between internal and external fertilisation.**
- **Know how the fetus develops during human pregnancy.**
- **Be able to draw and interpret graphs and charts.**

INTERNAL OR EXTERNAL FERTILISATION?

- When fertilisation happens inside the body it is called **internal fertilisation**.
- When it happens outside the body it is called **external fertilisation**.

Follow the mouse
www.bbc.co.uk/reallywild/amazing
www.5tigersorg/Basics
www.earthlife.net/mammals
www.pbs.org/lifeofbirds
www.alienexplorer.com

Activity

1 Work in small groups to research an animal. Find out:
- if fertilisation is internal or external
- how the developing fetus is protected
- how the developing fetus is fed
- how the young are cared for after they hatch or are born.

Each group will feed back to the class. Try to spot patterns in the information – is there any connection between the type of fertilisation and how the offspring

Activity

WS 8

2 You are going to do some extended writing.
- Think about the advantages and disadvantages of each type of fertilisation.
- In your writing, try to explain why both internal and external fertilisation exist, and how one way isn't 'better' than the other.

INTERPRETING DATA

Activity

3 Study the table.

(a) Draw a line graph to show how the length of the baby changes during human pregnancy. You will need to select a suitable scale, choose and label the axes correctly, and plot the results as a smooth curve.

(b) Divide the pregnancy into 4 equal sections (10 weeks each) and describe the differences in the shape of the graph.

(c) What does this tell you about the growth of the baby at different stages of the pregnancy?

Growth of baby

The table shows measurements of a baby growing in the uterus.

Weeks of pregnancy	Length of baby (mm)
4	11
6	21
10	110
17	325
30	475
40	500

STARTER

Your teacher will show you pictures of animals and tell you if they have internal or external fertilisation. You must decide if your teacher is telling the truth. Show your green card if you agree, red if you disagree, and amber if you are not sure!

HUMAN PREGNANCY

⚭ *Links to other key ideas*

Think about the links with Growth (page 26).

- The fertilised ovum cell starts to grow while it moves along the oviduct. It uses the yolky cytoplasm for energy.
- When it arrives in the uterus, it is a ball of cells called an embryo.
- The embryo settles into the thickened lining of the uterus. This process is called implantation.
- The placenta develops in the wall of the uterus to pass food and oxygen from mother to baby. The baby is called a fetus at this stage.
- The fetus is attached to the placenta by the umbilical cord.
- When the mother breathes and eats, oxygen and food end up in her blood. In the placenta, the mother's blood comes so close to the blood of the fetus that some of the oxygen and food pass across.
- The fetus uses the energy to grow and produce specialised cells and organs.
- The placenta also acts as a barrier to try to prevent harmful substances passing to the developing fetus.
- Waste materials produced by the fetus, like carbon dioxide and urea, pass back to the placenta through the umbilical cord.
- The baby is protected from knocks and bumps inside the uterus by the amniotic sac containing amniotic fluid. This bursts just before birth.
- After 9 months, the muscular walls of the uterus contract and push the baby out through the widened cervix and vagina.

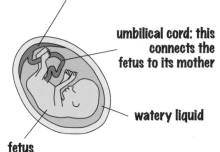

placenta: here the blood vessels of the fetus are close to the mother's, and food and oxygen diffuse into the fetus and waste products diffuse out

umbilical cord: this connects the fetus to its mother

watery liquid

fetus

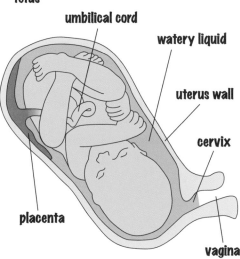

umbilical cord

watery liquid

uterus wall

cervix

placenta

vagina

Figure 1 *The fetus develops into a baby*

REVIEW

5 How would you explain to a younger brother or sister what happens during pregnancy? Write a story or script called 'My Mummy is having a baby!'

Need help?
Words that you might find useful:
    contractions food growth
  harmful milk months oxygen
   placenta protection warmth

Need more help?
Young children might ask questions like:
- Why is her tummy getting bigger?
- How is the baby growing inside her?
- How does the baby breathe in there?
- Why has Mummy stopped smoking?
- How long will it be before the baby comes out?
- What happens when the baby is born?
- How will we care for the baby?

BIRTH AND INHERITED CHARACTERISTICS

AIMS

By the end of this section you should:

* **Be able to describe what happens at** birth.
* **Identify the** characteristics **inherited from parents.**
* **Understand why brothers and sisters are not identical.**

INHERITED CHARACTERISTICS

* We look the way we do because we have inherited many of our characteristics from our parents. These <u>characteristics</u> were in the instructions carried by the chromosomes.
* At fertilisation, 23 chromosomes in the nucleus of the sperm cell joined with 23 chromosomes in the nucleus of the ovum.
* The full 46 chromosomes have all the information to grow into a baby.
* The instructions on the chromosomes are divided into **genes**, which themselves are made of a chemical called <u>DNA</u>.
* The characteristics you measured in Activity 2 will be different for everyone. This is called <u>variation</u>.
* When the variation is gradual, such as heights ranging from short to tall, a continuous **line graph** can be drawn, as shown in Figure 3.

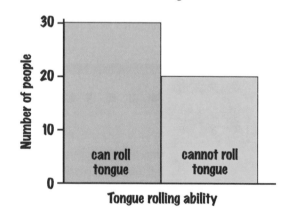

Activity

2 Collect data from yourself and others in your class about these characteristics:
Length of index finger (cm)
Right- or left-handed   Hair colour
Shoe size   Fleshy ear lobes or not
Rolling the tongue   Height (cm)
Eye colour

Activity

3 Display your collected data in bar charts. If the class results are gradual, draw a curve to show the shape of the graph.

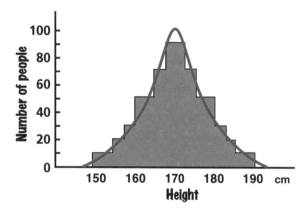

Figure 3 *Continuous variation*

Figure 4 *Discontinuous variation*

* When the variation has only a few options, for instance, you can either roll your tongue or you can't, the chart has no continuous range, and gives a **bar chart** like Figure 4.
* Even brothers and sisters would not have exactly the same characteristics because they inherit different combinations of chromosomes from their parents. It is completely random.

STARTER

Identify which **characteristics** Danny has inherited from Mum and which he has inherited from Dad.

GESTATION AND BIRTH

<u>Gestation</u> is the length of time from fertilisation until birth (how long the pregnancy lasts). Different animals have different gestation times as you can see in the chart of Figure 1.

Activity

1 Use the chart to answer these questions:
- What is the gestation time of **(a)** a mouse, **(b)** a cat, **(c)** a sheep?
- Can you see any pattern in your answer to the first question?
- Which animal in the chart does not fit the pattern?

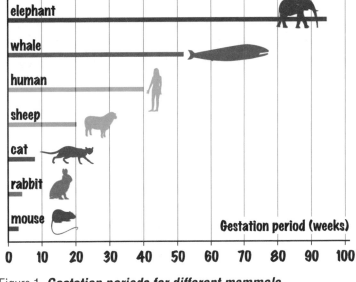

Figure 1 *Gestation periods for different mammals*

- Human pregnancy lasts approximately 40 weeks.
- Just before birth, the baby usually turns so that its head is down at the cervix.
- <u>Contractions</u> begin when the muscles in the wall of the uterus start pushing the baby out.
- The cervix dilates to allow the baby's head to pass through.
- The amniotic sac bursts so that the fluid runs out (the waters break).
- The mother helps the contractions by pushing the baby out of the vagina.
- The umbilical cord is cut and the baby begins to breathe for itself.
- The contractions continue until the placenta is pushed out as the <u>after-birth</u>.

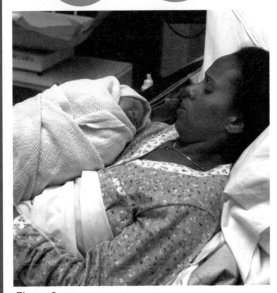

Figure 2

REVIEW

4 Use Worksheet **9** from the Starter and draw Danny's sister. Explain why she is similar but does not look exactly the same as her brother.

5 Revise what you have learned about Reproduction (pages 30–37).

Follow the mouse
www.discoveryhealth.co.uk
www.babycentre.co.uk
www.bbc.co.uk/education/bitesize

HABITATS

AIMS

By the end of this section you should:
- **Know about the physical conditions in some different habitats around the world.**
- **Know about some of the organisms that survive in the different habitats.**
- **Understand how the physical conditions can change over 24 hours.**

DAILY CHANGES IN THE ENVIRONMENT

bat

blackbird

owl

fox

seagull

rabbit

butterfly

deer

Figure 2

- *Animals respond to the changes in the <u>physical conditions</u> of their environment.*
- *Physical conditions include the level of light and of humidity.*
- *Some animals are active during the day and are called <u>diurnal</u>.*
- *Some are active at dawn.*
- *Others are active at dusk.*
- *<u>Nocturnal</u> animals are active at night.*

Activity

3 Look at the pictures in Figure 2. Decide when the animals are active, and classify each in one of these categories: diurnal; active at dawn; active at dusk; nocturnal.

WS 10 ### Activity

2 Think about how the physical conditions in your school grounds might change over 24 hours.
- Predict the shapes of the graphs for each condition.
- Can you spot any patterns between the graphs?
- Set up a data logger to check your predictions.

STARTER

Copy the table and brainstorm to complete more columns. Start in pairs and then feed back as a class (see page 5 for help).

Habitats around the world:	Desert
Physical conditions	dry; extremes of temperature (day and night)
Examples of plants and animals that survive there	cactus; camel; kangaroo rat

VARIETY OF LIFE

- The variety of living things on this planet is enormous – estimated at 30 million different species.
- This variety has partly come about because of the different conditions organisms try to survive in.

In the conditions of its <u>environment</u>, a successful organism is able to:

- maintain its temperature – it shouldn't get too hot or too cold
- get enough water
- get enough food
- reproduce.

I'm too hot!

This is better...

Figure 1

Activity

1 In twos or threes, research from secondary sources (e.g. books and the internet) one of the organisms named in the Starter activity.

- Focus on how the organism manages to survive in the physical conditions of its habitat.
- In a group, produce a poster or PowerPoint presentation to aid your feedback to the rest of the class.
- While other groups are feeding back, be looking for similarities and differences between the organisms researched.

Follow the mouse
www.wwf.org.uk
www.hitchams.suffolk.sch.uk/habitats
www.4learning.co.uk
www.panda.org/kids/wildlife

REVIEW

4 Choose one animal from the pictures on the opposite page.

- Describe what the physical conditions are like at the time when it is active.
- Describe the physical conditions in the habitat in which it lives.
- Explain how these conditions are suitable for the animal.
- If you leave out the name of the animal, you can swap your descriptions and try to identify which animal it is.

 5 For the next lesson you need to collect woodlice. Decide the best way to capture and transport them to school before you begin, in a way that no animals are harmed.

ADAPTATION

AIMS

By the end of this section you should:
- **Know about the behaviour responses of woodlice to their physical conditions.**
- **Carry out a controlled experiment to measure the response of a sample of woodlice.**
- **Interpret the results and come to a conclusion.**

EXPERIMENT TO INVESTIGATE THE CONDITIONS WOODLICE PREFER

To investigate the behaviour of animals, scientists can use two methods:

- They can observe animals in their natural habitat.
- They can control the conditions the animals are in by bringing them into the laboratory.

To investigate the behaviour of woodlice you can use a **choice chamber**.
You are going to find out whether woodlice prefer dark or light, and damp or dry conditions.

Begin with a plan of what you are going to do. Decide:
- why the woodlice need to enter the chamber in the middle
- what measurements you can take
- how many measurements you should take
- how many woodlice should you use (**sample** size)
- why one section of the chamber is left empty (**control**)
- what needs to be kept constant for a **fair test**
- what cannot be controlled.

Activity

1 What are the advantages and disadvantages of each method?

Activity

2 Swap your plan with another group and comment on the decisions they have made. Think all the time about whether their plan will answer the question you are investigating.
Once you have the results, come to a conclusion – explain what happened and why.
Can you scientifically say whether woodlice prefer dark, or damp, or both conditions?

STARTER

Discuss the answers to these questions:
- What type of container and conditions where chosen to transport the woodlice?
- Where did you find the woodlice?
- Do they prefer a dry or a damp place, light or dark?

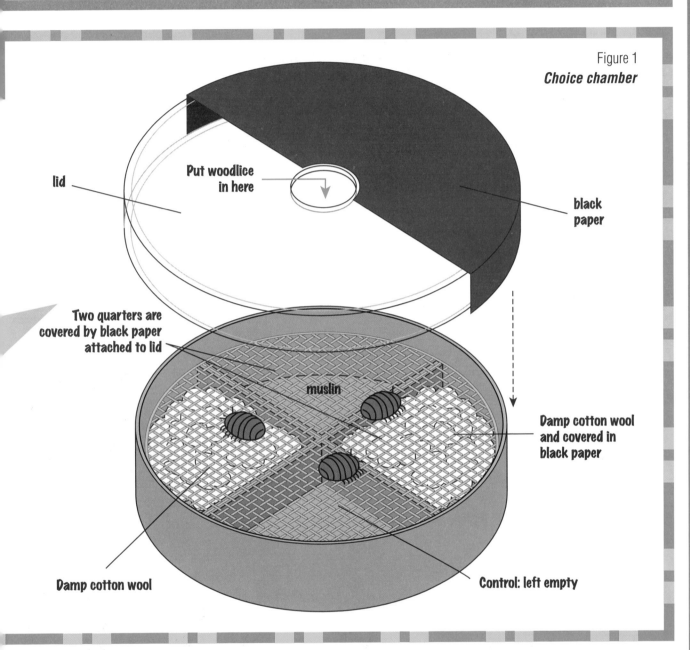

Figure 1
Choice chamber

lid

Put woodlice in here

black paper

Two quarters are covered by black paper attached to lid

muslin

Damp cotton wool and covered in black paper

Damp cotton wool

Control: left empty

REVIEW

3 Each group should share their conclusion with the rest of the class.

■ Did every group agree?

■ How reliable are the results?

■ What could you do to make the results more reliable?

Follow the mouse
www.wic.org/bio/jgoodall
www.janegoodall.org
www.pbs.org/wnet/nature/goodall

4 Observing the behaviour of animals in their natural habitat can take many years. Find out about the work of Jane Goodall studying chimpanzees.

SEASONAL VARIATION AND ADAPTATIONS

AIMS

By the end of this section you should:
• **Understand how the physical conditions in a habitat change with the seasons.**
• **Be able to describe how some organisms adapt to changes in a habitat.**

STARTER

WS 12

Look at your predicted graphs (from page 38) showing the physical conditions in your school grounds that change over 24 hours. Now predict and sketch the shapes of the graphs for each condition in the summer and in the winter. Can you spot any patterns between the graphs?

ADAPTING TO SEASONAL VARIATION

Organisms **adapt** to seasonal changes in their **habitat** in different ways:

• lying **dormant**
• **hibernating**
• **migrating**
• building up fat stores in their bodies
• growing thicker coats for **insulation**
• spending the winter in the **pupal stage** of their life cycle.

Figure 3

Activity

2 Use the glossary at the back of this book and a dictionary to find the meanings of the highlighted words in the list above. Check with a partner that you both agree and understand the words, because you will need them for the next activity.

Animals adapt to seasonal change. They can:

1 migrate to areas where food is available
2 migrate to breeding areas
3 hibernate when the temperature is low and food is scarce
4 store food for the winter
5 survive underground to avoid very hot or very cold temperatures
6 grow thicker fur for insulation in the winter.

Activity

3 Match the animals in Figure 3 to the correct adaptation numbered in the list on the left. There might be more than one adaptation linked to

SEASONAL VARIATION

Physical conditions:
Warm temperature
Less rainfall
Increased light levels

Figure 1 **Woodland in summer**

Physical conditions:
Lower temperature
Increased rainfall
Lower light levels

Figure 2 **Woodland in winter**

Activity

1. Use a digital camera to take photographs of the school grounds during different seasons of the year.

REVIEW

4. Work in pairs to complete the sentences below, using connectives (words that connect one part of a sentence to another). Connectives include: and, because, but, and so, such as, therefore, which, in order to.

- A deciduous tree loses its leaves in autumn...

- A conifer tree has needle-shaped leaves...

- Daffodil flowers can only be seen in spring...

- Bats are nocturnal...

- Whales migrate long distances...

- A fish has gills...

Read out your sentences and discuss which are scientifically correct and which have used the connectives correctly.

Follow the mouse

www.bgu.ac.il/~sergeev/pictures
www.bbc.co.uk/learning
www.zephyrus.co.uk/wintersleepers
www.pbs.org/wgbh/nova/satoyama/hibernation
www.alienexplorer.com/ecology

FOOD CHAINS AND WEBS

AIMS

By the end of this section you should:
- Understand that an organism lives where there is food it can eat.
- Identify animals as predators or prey.
- Be able to combine the food chains for a habitat into a food web.

PREDATORS AND PREY

- A **predator** is an animal that hunts and catches other animals for food.
- A **prey** animal is hunted by and eaten by the predators.

Activity

1 In pairs, sort through your animal pictures and classify them into two groups, predator or prey.
- Decide the characteristics that helped you identify the animal as a predator or prey.
- Collect feedback from the class to produce 2 lists of the characteristics of predators and of prey.

FOOD WEBS

- When food chains from a habitat have organisms in common, we can combine the chains to form a food web.
- A food web gives us a more complete picture of what organisms eat.
- Animals usually eat more than one thing so that they can swap if one type of food source starts to run out.
- The arrows in the food web still show the transfer of energy from one level to the next.

Activity

3 Use the information on the worksheet to identify the feeding relationships between the organisms. Try to draw the food web.

WS 13

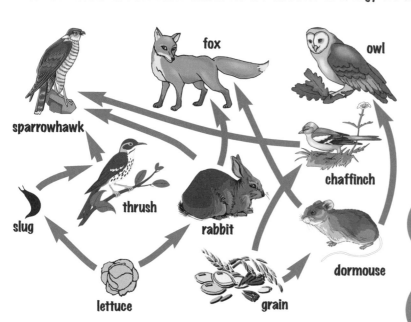

sparrowhawk
fox
owl
thrush
chaffinch
slug
rabbit
dormouse
lettuce
grain

Figure 3 *A food web*

Activity

4 Look at Figure 3.
(a) Find all the individual food chains in this web.
(b) Which animals are competing for the same food source?

STARTER

As well as adapting to the physical conditions in which it lives, an organism is also adapted to the food it can eat.

- Look at the demonstration set up by your teacher. Each object is like the beak of a bird.
- Which beak is best adapted to each food source?
- Name any birds you can think of that have similar beaks.

FOOD CHAINS

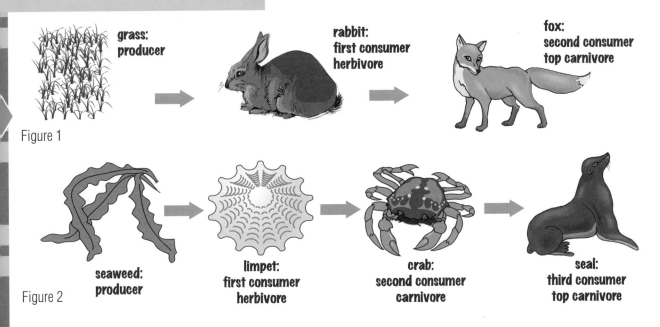

grass: producer → rabbit: first consumer herbivore → fox: second consumer top carnivore

Figure 1

seaweed: producer → limpet: first consumer herbivore → crab: second consumer carnivore → seal: third consumer top carnivore

Figure 2

- Food chains usually get their energy from the Sun.
- A green plant uses this energy to carry out photosynthesis and make food. This is why green plants are called <u>producers</u>, and they are at the start of the chain.
- Animals are <u>consumers</u> because they have to eat food.
- First or **primary consumers** are <u>herbivores</u> that eat the producers and their products which include fruits, seeds and dead leaves.
- **Secondary consumers** are <u>carnivores</u> that eat the herbivores.
- The arrows in the food chain show the direction that the energy flows in between the organisms.
- If there is enough energy, a food chain will continue with **tertiary consumers**, but this is normally as far as the chain can go.
- Animals that eat both plants and other animals are called <u>omnivores</u>.

Activity

2 Think of examples of food you have eaten today, and work backwards along the food chain to see that all our food ultimately comes from plants. Look for any overlap in the food chains your class creates.

REVIEW

5 There are many scientific terms that you must use correctly when talking about food chains and webs. Your teacher will give you a list of these terms with their meanings all mixed up. Try to match the correct word to its meaning and you will get 1 point for each correct answer.

POPULATION CHANGES IN A FOOD WEB

AIMS

By the end of this section you should:
- Know what a population is.
- Identify what can cause the size of a population to change.
- Be able to predict the effects on the rest of the food web when the size of one population changes.

STARTER

Brainstorm as a class:

What can cause the numbers of plants and animals to change?

REVIEW

5 Return to page 39 and the Starter in the Habitats lesson. Choose one of the habitats you named and draw a food web for some of the organisms that manage to live there. Label your web with these words, if you can:

producer   herbivore   primary consumer

secondary consumer   carnivore   tertiary consumer

omnivore   energy transfer

6 Revise all your work on the Environment and Feeding Relationships (pages 38–46).

Follow the mouse

www.gould.edu.au/foodwebs/kids_web
www.library.thinkquest.org
www.countrysidefoundation.org.uk
www.alienexplorer.com/ecology/topic4

POPULATIONS IN A FOOD WEB

A **population** is the number of organisms of a particular species living in an area.
A change in the population in one part of the food web affects all the other organisms.

Activity

1 Look at Figure 1.
(a) What would happen to the population of slugs if humans harvested all the lettuce?
(b) Which animal is **competing** with the fox for rabbits?
(c) What happens to the amount of grain if the chaffinches die from a disease?
(d) How does the owl help a farmer?
(e) What happens to the population of slugs if the sparrowhawks move to a different **territory**?

Activity

2 Use the worksheet to work out why the sizes of the populations change over time. **WS 15**

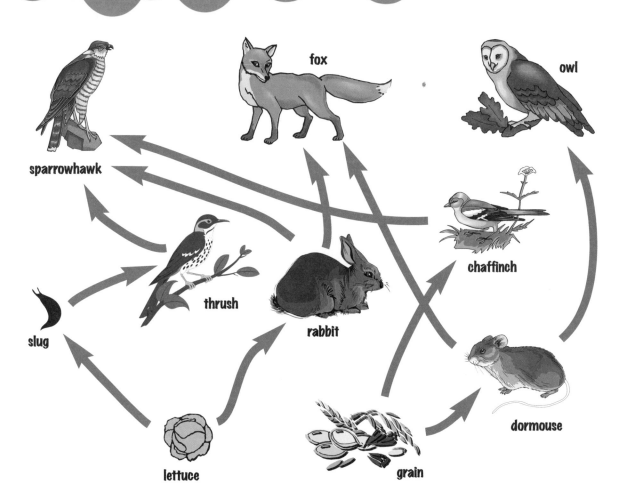

Figure 1 *A food web*

Activity

4 Use simulation software to demonstrate what happens in a food web when a change is made.

Activity

3 Explain what effects seasonal visitors, for example, swifts, have on the populations in a food web.

VARIATION BETWEEN AND WITHIN SPECIES

AIMS

By the end of this section you should:
- **Remember that there are two categories of genetic variation.**
- **Know what a species is.**
- **Predict and interpret the shapes of graphs when investigating relationships between variables.**

STARTER

⚭ *Links to other key ideas*
Think about the links with Birth and Inherited Characteristics (page 36).

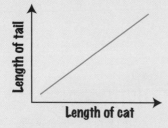

Figure 1 **Continuous variation**

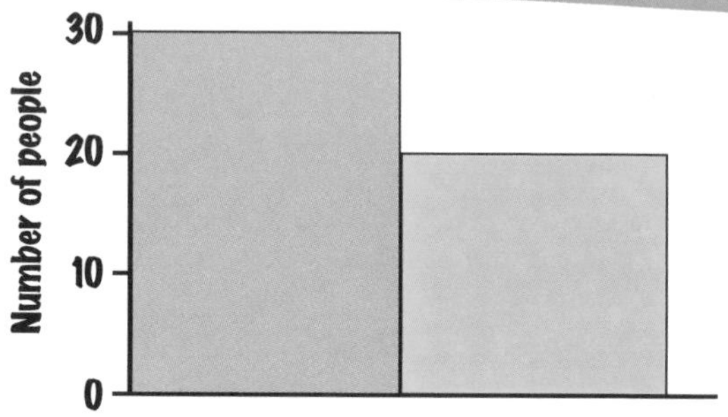

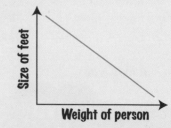

Figure 2 **Discontinuous variation**

- Where have you seen graphs like this before?
- In pairs, think of different labels for the axes of each graph.
- Feed back to the rest of the class, then discuss which axes are correct, and the reasons why.

REVIEW

5 Look at these graphs and the captions. Decide if the relationship matches the shape of the graph. If you think they do, show your 'True' card. Otherwise, show your 'False' card. Be ready to explain your decision.

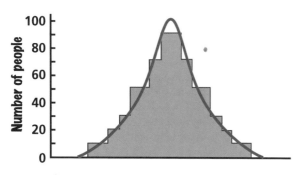

Figure 5 **The longer the cat, the longer its tail**

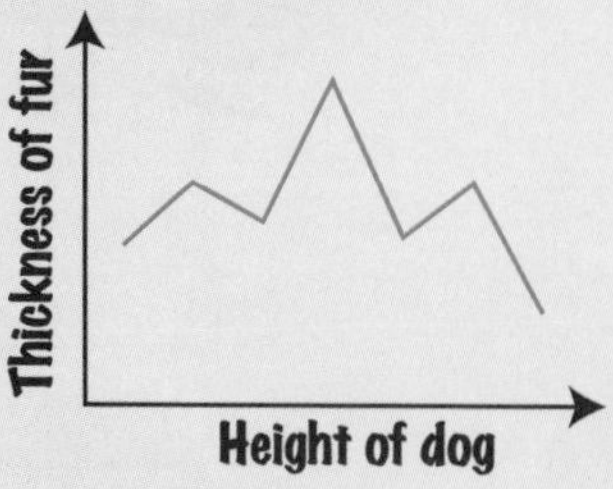

Figure 6 **Bigger dogs have thicker fur**

Figure 7 **There is no correlation between a person's weight and the size of their feet**

 6 Revise what you learned about the Variety of Life at Key Stage 2.

VARIATION

- A <u>species</u> is a group of organisms so similar that they are able to reproduce with each other.
- There is variation *within the species* because each organism has inherited different genes from its parents.
- The variation *between different species*, however, is greater. This is why organisms are classed in different groups.

Activity

1 Your school or local library should have books about dogs and cats. Half the class should use the dog books and the other half should use the cat books. Work in small groups to list all the similarities between the different types of cats or dogs, and all the differences. Share your lists with the rest of the class and discuss.

INVESTIGATING RELATIONSHIPS BETWEEN VARIABLES

Figure 3 *Holly leaves show several <u>variables</u>*

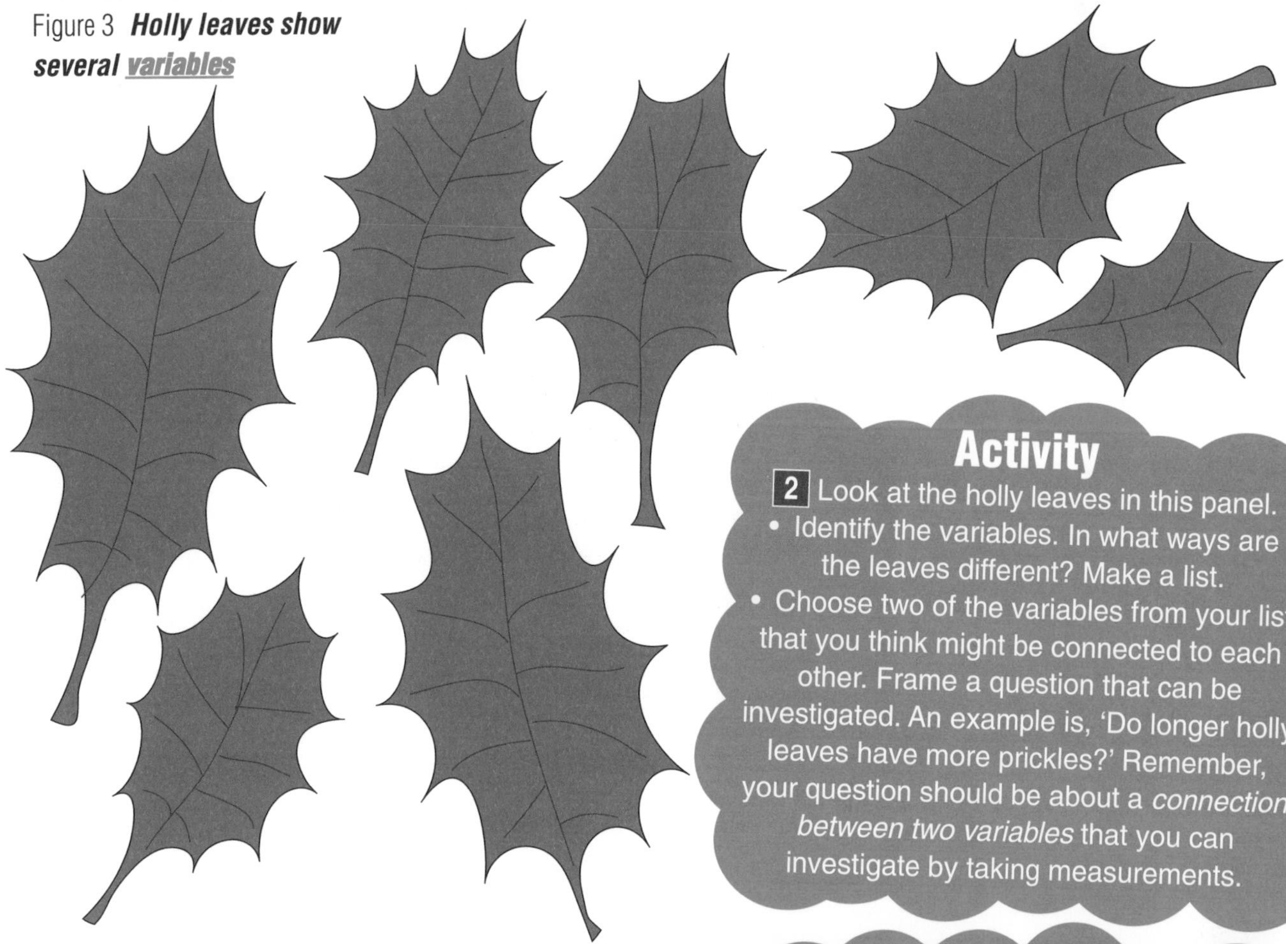

Activity

2 Look at the holly leaves in this panel.
- Identify the variables. In what ways are the leaves different? Make a list.
- Choose two of the variables from your list that you think might be connected to each other. Frame a question that can be investigated. An example is, 'Do longer holly leaves have more prickles?' Remember, your question should be about a *connection between two variables* that you can investigate by taking measurements.

Figure 4 *Axes for a graph linking length of holly leaves and number of prickles*

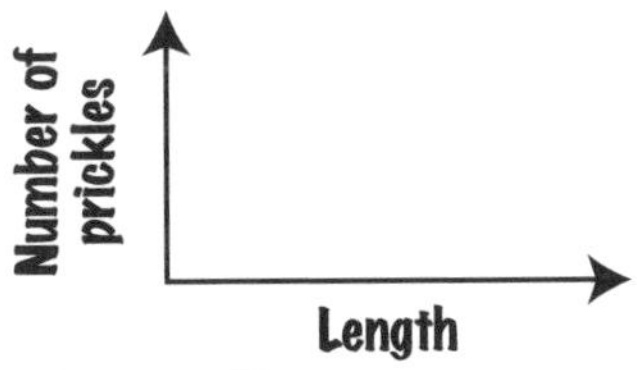

Number of prickles

Length

Activity

4 Take measurements of the leaves on this page. Think about these questions:
- (a) How will you make your measurements accurate?
- (b) How many holly leaves should you measure (sample size)?
- (c) When will you have enough results to come to a firm conclusion? Plot the results on a graph.
- (d) What is the relationship between the two variables you have investigated?

Activity

3 Look at Figure 4. Predict the shape of the graph if:
- (a) longer holly leaves do have more prickles.
- (b) there is the opposite relationship – shorter holly leaves have more prickles.
- (c) there is no correlation – the length of the leaves is not connected to the number of prickles.

GROUPING ORGANISMS

AIMS

By the end of this section you should:

- **Understand that variation within a species is due to both** genetic **and** environmental factors**.**
- **Use the similarities and differences between organisms to sort them into groups.**
- **Begin to understand the development of the** <u>classification system</u>**.**

CLASSIFYING

- There is no right or wrong way to classify living things into groups.
- Scientists use classification to make it easier to describe and identify organisms.
- Linnaeus originally developed the system used today in 1758.
- As new organisms are discovered, the system can be adapted slightly.

Follow the mouse

www.species2000.org
www.vet.ed.ac.uk/students/taxonomy
www.linnean.org/html/history

Activity

3 Work with three other pupils to sort your pictures of living things into groups.

- Put organisms together when they have things in common.
- Be ready to explain why you have chosen the groups.
- When the class feeds back, consider the advantages and disadvantages of the systems used. In particular, notice if some organisms could actually be put in two groups because they have characteristics belonging to both groups.

REVIEW

4 **Put the heading 'Genetic factors' on one side of a whiteboard and 'Environmental factors' on the other.**

■ **Read the following description of Carla and list the features she has inherited from her parents and the features which depend on how she was brought up.**

Carla has brown hair cut short. She speaks Italian and can roll her tongue. Carla is 5 feet tall and weighs 7 stone. She wears size 4 shoes and loves dancing. Her eyes are green and she writes with her left hand. Carla is quite outgoing and has a wicked sense of humour.

■ **Did the rest of the class agree with your lists?**

■ **Did you have any problems deciding which side of the board to put some of the characteristics on?**

5 **Write a story called 'A day in the life of identical twins'. Describe some of the fun they can have because of their genetic similarities and how people tell them apart using their differences caused by the environment.**

STARTER

Work in pairs to look at the examples of variation provided by your teacher. In each case, try to work out what has caused the variation. Does the rest of the class agree?

There is variation between organisms because in **genetic variation** they have **inherited** different **genes** from their parents. How and where an organism lives also affects its characteristics. These effects make up the organism's **environmental variation**.

SORTING INTO GROUPS

Although there is variation between organisms of the same species, they have so many characteristics in common that they are grouped together. This means that scientists must make careful observations of the characteristics of living things before deciding which group they belong in.

Activity

2 Play the identification game.
- Each of you will be given a picture or photograph of a plant or animal.
- The rest of the class take it in turns to ask one question to which you can only answer 'Yes' or 'No'.
- After each question, a guess can be made to identify the organism in the picture.

Activity

1 Organisms can be identified as belonging to a particular group from various descriptions.
- Find some poems about plants and animals and read them out to the class.
- Try to identify which group is being described.
- How do the scientific descriptions below compare to the descriptions used in the poems and the pictures?

The animals below have been given scientific descriptions to help identify them.

Figure 2 *A reptile with a flexible jaw and no legs. It has a forked tongue that it uses to smell, and kills its prey by suffocation or poison.*

Figure 1 *A red or yellow beetle. Most ladybirds are predators feeding on aphids. Their bright coats warn of their bitter taste. Adults hibernate in large groups in the winter.*

Figure 3 *A striped mammal with hooves. A herbivore. Its habitat is the grassland of Africa.*

51

TAXONOMIC GROUPS

AIMS

By the end of this section you should:
- **Know what classification is.**
- **Be able to identify some of the main taxonomic groups.**
- **Describe the features of animals in the five vertebrate groups.**

STARTER

Look at the key words your teacher has put on the board. Learn how to say the words and how to spell them. Try different techniques, but if you get stuck, ask your teacher.

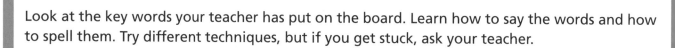

Organism (living thing)

Plant Kingdom   **Animal Kingdom**

Invertebrates (without a backbone)

Examples:

Activity

1 Use a large space like the gym or the playground to set out a classification system on the floor. Your teacher will give everyone a picture of an organism to classify into the correct taxonomic group. Follow the branches until you arrive at the correct group for your organism.

Activity

2 Work in twos or threes to research one of the vertebrate groups using secondary sources (e.g. books and CD ROMs). You will need details of:
- the body covering
- whether the animals have live births or lay eggs
- whether the animals can keep their own bodies warm
- special features the animals have for feeding
- special features the animals have for breathing
- special features the animals have for moving.

All groups should add their information to an overhead transparency for use by the

TAXONOMY

- When scientists classify organisms into groups it is called **taxonomy**.
- The organisms are classified together because of their similarities.

Vertebrates are animals with a backbone. There are five groups of vertebrates, and each group has features that are specific only to them:

- **Fish** have scales, fins and breathe through gills. All fish live in water.
- **Amphibians** have a smooth, moist skin. They live on land but must return to the water to lay their eggs.
- **Reptiles** have dry, scaly skin. They live on land and lay eggs with shells.
- **Birds** have feathers and wings. They are warm-blooded and lay eggs with hard shells.
- **Mammals** have fur/hair. They give birth to live young and feed them with milk produced in the mammary glands.

Marsupials are a separate group of mammals found mainly in Australia. Like all mammals, they feed their young on milk, but the female does not carry her young inside her body for the entire pregnancy. Some marsupials lay eggs and others give birth to a tiny embryo. Examples include the duck-billed platypus and the kangaroo.

Kangaroo

Vertebrates (with a backbone)

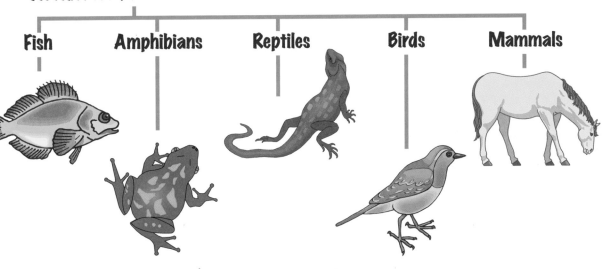

Fish   Amphibians   Reptiles   Birds   Mammals

REVIEW

5 Look back to the pictures of living things on Worksheet 16 (page 50). Classify these into the taxonomic groups shown in this lesson.

Follow the mouse
www.bbc.co.uk/education/ks3bitesize
www.nhm.ac.uk

SAMPLING AND USING KEYS FOR IDENTIFICATION

AIMS

By the end of this section you should:
- Have used sampling equipment to collect invertebrates.
- Have used a key to classify invertebrates into groups.

USING KEYS

- **Keys** are used to help people identify living things.
- There are two main types of key but they both involve a series of questions with only two possible answers.
- Each time you answer a question you get closer to identifying the organism.
- Eventually, a question will leave you with only one option, which is the organism you are trying to identify.

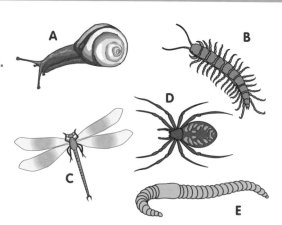

TYPE 1

- Choose one organism, for example **A**, to try to identify, and go to 'Start' on the diagram below.
- Answer the first question: Has it got legs?
- The answer is no, so follow the 'no' arrow.
- Answer the next question: Has it got a shell?
- The answer is yes, so follow the 'yes' arrow. You can't go any further, so the answer is a snail.
- Go back to the start and choose another animal to identify.

TYPE 2

- We can use a different type of key to identify the animals above.
- Again choose an organism, for example **E**.
- Follow these instructions:

  1. Does it have a shell? ...No, go to **2** ...Yes, it's a snail
  2. Does it have legs? ...No, it's a worm ...Yes, go to **3**
  3. Does it have more than four pairs of legs? ...No, go to **4** ...Yes, it's a centipede
  4. Does it have wings? ...No, it's a spider ...Yes, it's a damselfly.

- Did you find out that organism **E** was a worm?

STARTER

Look at the key words your teacher has put on the board. You have three minutes to work out how the words should be organised to show the classification system.

SAMPLING FOR INVERTEBRATES

A range of equipment can be used to collect <u>invertebrate</u> animals.

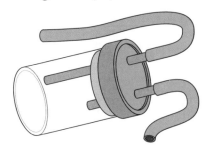

Figure 1 *A pooter*

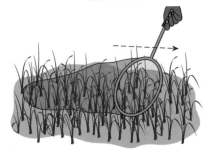

Figure 2 *A sweep net*

Figure 3 *Using a beater*

Collecting with a <u>pooter</u>:
- Use only on invertebrates that are small enough to fit through the tube.
- Place one tube over the invertebrate and then suck through the other tube. Make sure you get them the right way round!
- Once the invertebrate has been sucked into the pot, you can use a key to identify it.

You can, of course, also look for invertebrates under logs and stones, on walls, in sheds and anywhere else you can think of. It is important that you remember these points:

- NEVER HARM ANY LIVING THING.
- TAKE CARE WITH ORGANISMS THAT STING OR BITE.
- RETURN ALL ANIMALS TO THE EXACT PLACE YOU FOUND THEM.
- WASH YOUR HANDS AFTERWARDS.

Collecting with a sweep net:
- Use it to collect invertebrates from long grass and bushes.
- Brush the net through the grass in a sweeping motion and then flip the net over to prevent the invertebrates from escaping.
- Use a pooter or magnifying pot to view the invertebrates collected.

Collecting with a beater:
- Use a beater to collect invertebrates from bushes and trees.
- Place a white sheet under the tree so that you can see any invertebrates that fall.
- Gently beat the branches and use a pooter or magnifying pot to view the invertebrates collected.

Activity

1 Use sampling equipment for the following:
- Work in small groups to sample the invertebrates in your school grounds.
- For each one you find, keep a record of where you found it and what it was doing.
- Afterwards, you will be able to discuss the reasons for different invertebrates surviving in different habitats. It may be that the habitats provide shelter, a food source or a hiding place from predators.

REVIEW

2 Use the jigsaw pieces to match the pictures of the animals from a variety of taxonomic groups to their correct descriptions.

WS **18**

3 Revise what you have learned about Variation and Classification (pages 48–55).

ACIDS AND ALKALIS

AIMS

By the end of this section you should:
- **Know some examples of everyday acids and alkalis.**
- **Know some names of acids and alkalis in the lab.**
- **Know about the hazards of handling and transporting acids and alkalis.**
- **Be able to work safely with acids and alkalis.**

STARTER

Acids taste bitter or sour. Acids in foods are very dilute (weak). Stronger acids are very corrosive – this means they attack surfaces and dissolve them away.

As a class, discuss what you already know about acids.

- Where have you heard the word 'acid' before?
- Which foods or drinks taste sour? (These contain food acids.)
- Why is the builder in the picture wearing gloves and goggles?
- Why is it safe to put vinegar on your chips, but not brick acid?

Figure 1 **Vinegar is a weak acid that is safe to use in foods**

Figure 2 **Brick acid is used to dissolve cement off old bricks**

TRANSPORTING ACIDS AND ALKALIS

Acids and alkalis are transported using road tankers. The tankers are all labelled to show what they are carrying, and have a code to tell the fire services how to deal with any accidents or spills.

The tanker is lined with glass or plastic to stop the acid dissolving the metal.

The spilled acid is diluted with lots of water and washed down the drains.

Fire service workers wear body protection to stop the acid damaging their skin.

The code tells the fire services how to clean up spills.

This symbol shows that the acid is corrosive.

SULPHURIC ACID

2PE
1830
SULPHURIC ACID
0362-8497-618   MAG CHEM

FIRE

Activity

2 Discuss the following in groups. What is the main hazard of handling acids? What safety precautions should you take when you are handling acids in the lab? Car batteries contain sulphuric acid. Design a sign to go in a garage to tell mechanics how to deal safely with a battery acid spill.

USING ACIDS AND ALKALIS

Acids are used in many everyday products.
Some products contain <u>alkalis</u>. These are 'chemical opposites' of acids.
Acids and alkalis cancel each other out.

Activity

1 Sulphuric acid is used to make fertilisers, plastics, paints, detergents and soaps, fibres, dyes and photo films. Write a script for a 2-minute video about uses of sulphuric acid. What will you say? What will you show happening?

Acids are used in cleaning materials because they dissolve limescale.

Vinegar is an acid used in foods because it kills germs and so preserves foods.

Shower gel, shampoo and washing up liquid all contain detergents made using sulphuric acid.

Some toothpastes contain alkali to get rid of acid in your mouth that could rot your teeth.

Acids and alkalis are used on a very big scale in the chemical industry to make products for the shops. The main 'big scale' acids used in industry are sulphuric acid, nitric acid and hydrochloric acid. The main 'big scale' alkali is sodium hydroxide.

REVIEW

WS 19

3 (a) Which of the following substances turn litmus **red**?

lemon juice   toothpaste   vinegar   sodium hydroxide   sulphuric acid

(b) Write down 3 substances that turn litmus **blue**.

4 Look at labels of foods and household products.
■ Make a list of all the acid names you can find.
■ Why are the acids in the product (e.g. to preserve food or to improve a cleaner)?

Follow the mouse
www.chem4kids.com/files/react_acidbase.html
www.bbc.co.uk/education/ks3bitesize/science

INDICATORS AND pH

AIMS

By the end of this section you should:
• **Know what an indicator is used for.**
• **Understand how to use the pH scale.**

UNIVERSAL INDICATOR

Universal indicator is a mixture of indicator dyes which gives a range of colours in different acids and alkalis. It can show the difference between a **strong acid** and a **weak acid**, or a **strong alkali** and a **weak alkali**. Universal indicator can also show if a substance is **neutral** (neither an acid nor an alkali).

Activity

2 **(a)** Give reasons why universal indicator is more useful than litmus.
(b) Sour foods contain weak acids but never strong acids.
• Explain how you could test some sour foods to find out if this is true.
• What would you expect to see?

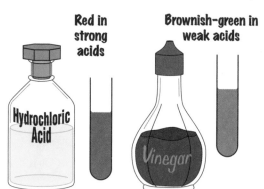
Red in strong acids — Hydrochloric Acid

Brownish-green in weak acids — Vinegar

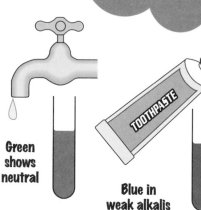
Green shows neutral

Blue in weak alkalis — TOOTHPASTE

Purple in strong alkalis — Sodium Hydroxide

Figure 3 *Universal indicator shows a range of colours*

THE pH SCALE

The **pH scale** shows how acidic or alkaline a solution is.
• Neutral substances are pH 7.
• pH 1 to 6 are acids.
• pH 8 to 14 are alkalis.
Universal indicator is used to find out the pH of a solution by checking colours against a colour chart.

Activity

3 Fresh milk is nearly neutral. Sour milk is more acidic. Explain how to use universal indicator to prove this. What would you expect to see?
Use Figures 3 and 4 to work out the pH of:
(a) hydrochloric acid **(b)** vinegar
(c) water **(d)** toothpaste
(e) sodium hydroxide

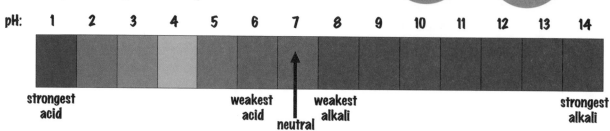

pH: 1 2 3 4 5 6 7 8 9 10 11 12 13 14

strongest acid   weakest acid   neutral   weakest alkali   strongest alkali

Figure 4 *The pH scale and universal indicator colours*

STARTER

As a class, help your teacher make a spider diagram on the board showing what you know about acids and alkalis. Make sure your map contains information about:

- examples of everyday acids and alkalis
- how acids and alkalis are different
- why acids and alkalis are hazardous
- how to handle acids and alkalis safely
- how spillages can be cleaned up safely.

INDICATORS

An **indicator** is used to tell the difference between acids and alkalis. Indicators turn a different colour in acids and in alkalis. Many natural dyes from plants can be used as indicators.

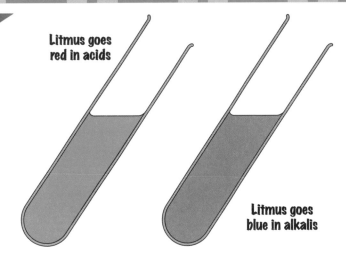

Litmus goes red in acids

Litmus goes blue in alkalis

Figure 1 *Litmus is an indicator dye obtained from lichens*

blackcurrants

red cabbage

beetroot

Figure 2 *Dyes from these plants can also be used as indicators*

Activity
WS 20

1 Work in pairs to extract some dye from a plant. Test your dye to see if it works as an indicator.

REVIEW

4 What are indicators used for?

5 Use these words to explain why universal indicator is a very good indicator.
colours   pH scale   strong   weak   acids   alkalis

NEUTRALISATION

AIMS

At the end of this section you should:
- Understand that acids can be neutralised by alkalis.

WATCHING NEUTRALISATION HAPPEN

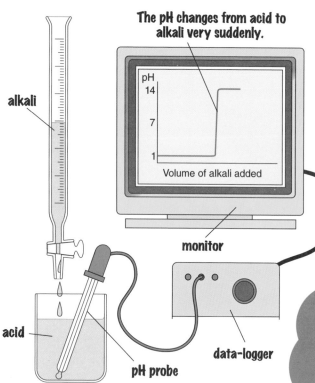

The pH changes from acid to alkali very suddenly.

alkali

Volume of alkali added

monitor

acid

pH probe

data-logger

Figure 2 *Neutralising a strong acid with strong alkali*

A data-logger attached to a pH probe gives a graph to show how the pH changes during <u>neutralisation</u>.

A data-logger is very useful for following neutralisation reactions because:

- it measures pH more accurately than comparing indicator colours
- it gives a printed record of what happens during the reaction
- it can produce a graph quickly.

Activity

2 (a) Describe what the data-logger tells you is happening to the pH during neutralisation.
(b) How can you tell that the beaker contained acid at the start?
(c) It is very difficult to make an *exactly* neutral solution by mixing an acid and alkali together. How does the graph indicate that this is difficult?

pH CHANGES IN YOUR MOUTH

A pH probe has been used to find out how the pH changes in your mouth during the day.

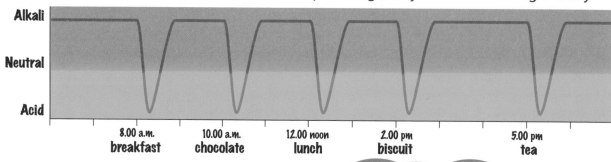

Alkali					
Neutral					
Acid					
	8.00 a.m. **breakfast**	10.00 a.m. **chocolate**	12.00 noon **lunch**	2.00 pm **biscuit**	5.00 pm **tea**

Figure 3 *Mouth pH during the day*

Activity

3 Explain what happens to the pH in your mouth after you eat food. Why does eating between meals rot your teeth quickly?

STARTER

Work in pairs to find as many ways of finishing the sentences as possible.

Acids are different to alkalis because...

Acids are similar to alkalis because...

NEUTRALISING ACIDS

Antacids are bases that neutralise extra acid in your stomach.

Bases are used to neutralise extra acid in the soil.

Toothpaste contains bases to stop acids rotting your teeth.

Figure 1 *Uses for bases*

∞ Links to other key ideas

You can find out more in Acids and Carbonates (page 66).

We need acids in our stomachs to digest food, but too much acid makes us feel ill. Medicines for upset stomachs contain substances to **neutralise** (cancel out) extra acid.

Too much acid can cause other problems:

- Too much acid in soils kills plants.
- Acids in our mouths rot our teeth.
- Acid rain falling in lakes will kill fish.

Acids can be neutralised by adding **alkalis**.

A substance that can neutralise an acid is called a **base**.

Alkalis are bases that dissolve in water.

Activity

WS 21

1 Carry out the investigation to find out how antacid tablets work.

- Vinegar stops wasp stings from hurting. What does this tell you about wasp stings?

REVIEW

4 Use these words to complete the passage.

alkalis   indicators   neutralise   pH probes

Bases _____ acids. Bases that dissolve in water are called _____.
Neutralisation can be followed using _____ or _____.

5 Garden test kits are used to test soil for acidity. Design a test kit for selling to gardeners. What needs to be in your kit? Write an instruction leaflet for your kit explaining how to use it and what results to look for.

CHEMICAL REACTIONS

AIMS

By the end of this section you should:
• **Know how to tell when a chemical change has happened.**

STARTER

Look at this group of changes.
• Which changes are reversible and which are not?
• Which changes involve new, different substances being made? How can you tell?

Freezing orange juice to make an ice lolly

Burning wood

Baking a cake

A puddle drying up on a hot day

Peeling an orange

ENERGY CHANGES

Chemical changes often involve **energy** changes. Energy can be given out as heat, light or sound. Some chemical changes take in energy.

Activity

2 **(a)** Describe ways to find out if there is a temperature change during an experiment.
(b) 'Neutralising acid with an alkali involves an energy change.' Explain how you could find out whether this is true.
(c) Carry out experiments to find out more about chemical changes.

WS 22

FIREWORKS

Before it is lit, a firework is made of cardboard, paper and powdered chemicals.

• The firework turns into ash and gases.
• Burning a firework cannot be reversed.
• A lot of energy is given out as sound, light and heat.

Figure 3 **The explosion of a firework is a chemical change**

LOOKING FOR ENERGY CHANGES

∞ Links to other key ideas

Learn how to use a Bunsen burner safely in The Bunsen Burner (page 90

Sometimes energy changes are easy to spot.

Small energy changes can be seen by looking at temperature changes.

Three points to remember.
■ Chemical changes are not easily reversed.
■ Chemical changes make new substances.
■ Chemical changes often involve energy changes.

Figure 4 **Chemical reactions have different energy changes**

REVERSIBLE OR NOT?

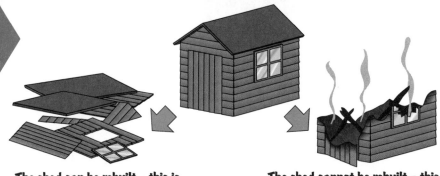

The shed can be rebuilt - this is only a temporary change.

The shed cannot be rebuilt - this is a permanent change.

Figure 1 *Reversible and irreversible changes*

Chemical changes are not easily reversed – they are **permanent** changes. For example, if a wooden shed was blown down in the wind, you could rebuild it with the same materials – the change is *reversible*. If the shed was burnt down, it is not possible to rebuild it – the wood does not even exist any more!

NEW PRODUCTS

The substances used up in a chemical change are called <u>reactants</u>. Chemical changes always make new <u>products</u>. A fallen-down shed is still made of wood and nails. A burnt-down shed has changed into smoke particles, gases, blackened wood and ash.

A new substance is made when iron rusts.

A burning match makes smoke, ash and gases.

Antacid tablets make a gas when they neutralise acid.

Figure 2 *Chemical changes give new products*

Activity

1 **(a)** What do you *see* when antacid tablets make a gas in the acid?

(b) Make a table with column headings: Chemical change; New products; Reversed easily or not. Complete the table for the chemical changes in Figure 2.

(c) Decide which are chemical reactions:
frying an egg   cutting up a pizza
melting ice cream   burning petrol in a car

∞ Links to other key ideas

You can find out more in Combustion (page 68) and Fuels (page 70).

REVIEW

3 Decide which of these statements are **true** and which are **false** for chemical changes. Make the true statements into full sentences and write them down.

- Can be easily reversed.
- New substances are made.
- Are permanent.
- Burning is an example.
- Often give out light or heat.
- Examples include boiling and freezing.

Follow the mouse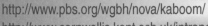
http://www.pbs.org/wgbh/nova/kaboom/
http://www.cornwallis.kent.sch.uk/intranet/elearn/science/chemreact/chemicalreaction1.html

4 Lee <u>chops up some wood</u> and <u>burns it</u> on a bonfire.

Decide which of the underlined phrases describes a chemical change and which does not. Draw a cartoon showing what Lee is doing. Write labels or captions on your diagram to show all the ways you can tell that a chemical change is happening.

ACIDS AND METALS

AIMS

By the end of this section you should:
- **Understand what happens when acids react with metals.**
- **Know how to test for hydrogen gas.**

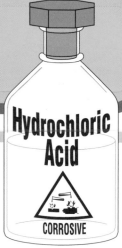

Hydrochloric Acid

CORROSIVE

STARTER

- What does the 'corrosive' label on the bottle of acid mean?
- How can we handle acids safely?
- How are acid spills cleaned up?

 Links to other key ideas
You learned about acids in Acids and Alkalis (page 56).

ACID ATTACK

Acids corrode metals very quickly, using up the metal to form new products. One product is the corroded metal. It cannot be seen because it *dissolves* in the acid. The metal fizzes because a *gas* is also formed.

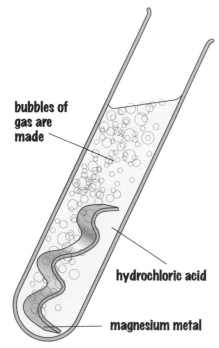

bubbles of gas are made

hydrochloric acid

magnesium metal

Figure 2
An acid and a metal form a gas

TESTING THE GAS

Hydrogen makes a lighted splint go 'pop'.

POP!

Figure 3 *Testing the gas*

The gas made when acids react with metals is called <u>hydrogen</u>. It is a <u>flammable</u> gas – it makes a 'pop' sound when we light it.

METAL CORROSION

Most metals do not stay new and shiny for very long. They go dull as <u>corrosion</u> takes place, and very often a layer of corroded material appears on the surface. Metals corrode to become brittle materials. Corroded cars are dangerous because the iron bodywork has become too thin to protect you in an accident. Corroded metal parts in engines get stuck so that the engine cannot work. Metals corrode most in wet conditions.

Corroded iron is called rust.

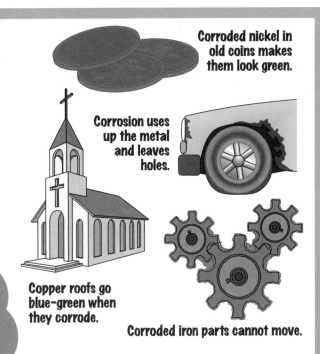

Corroded nickel in old coins makes them look green.

Corrosion uses up the metal and leaves holes.

Copper roofs go blue-green when they corrode.

Corroded iron parts cannot move.

Figure 1 *Corroded metals*

Activity

1 (a) Do you think corrosion is a chemical change? Explain your answer.
(b) List each metal in Figure 1 and the colour it goes when it corrodes.
(c) How could you prove that corrosion happens faster outside?

ACIDS THAT CAUSE CORROSION

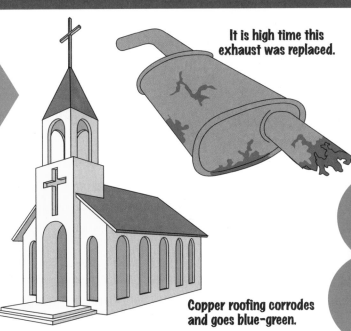

It is high time this exhaust was replaced.

Copper roofing corrodes and goes blue-green.

Figure 4 *Corrosion from acid gases in the air*

Metals that are in contact with acids corrode very quickly. Some exhaust gases from cars are acids – car exhausts rust much faster than the rest of the car. Acid rain makes metals corrode faster, too.

Activity

WS 23

2 You can investigate how different metals react with acids.
(a) Hydrogen is very light. It was once used to fill airship balloons that carried passengers. Explain why using hydrogen is dangerous.
(b) Gold does not corrode and does not react with acids. How does this explain why gold is popular for making jewellery and fillings for teeth?

REVIEW

3 Liz writes this information in her science book:

Acids corrode all metals. All metals make hydrogen. Hydrogen pops when it is lit.

Her teacher says, 'Only one of these statements is correct.'
Re-write the information so that it is completely correct.

Follow the mouse
http://www.exploratorium.edu/science_explorer/copper_caper.html
www.pbs.org/wnet/secrets/ from the drop-down menu, choose 'Hindenberg' as a case to explore

ACIDS AND CARBONATES

AIMS

By the end of this section you should:
- **Understand what happens when acids react with** carbonates.
- **Know how to** test for carbon dioxide gas.

FIZZY LEMONADE

Fizzy drinks all contain bubbles of <u>carbon dioxide</u> gas. Carbon dioxide is an ideal gas for making the fizz in drinks because it is non-toxic, non-flammable and does not react with other substances very easily.

Carbon dioxide is an acidic gas. This is one reason why fizzy drinks have a sharp taste. To prove that the fizz is carbon dioxide, shake the lemonade, collect the gas and test it with <u>lime water</u>.

the tube collects the carbon dioxide

lime water goes cloudy

fizzy lemonade

Figure 1 *Testing for carbon dioxide*

Carbon dioxide turns lime water cloudy

Activity

1 Discuss in groups:
(a) Why is carbon dioxide a better fizzy drink gas than hydrogen?
(b) Joe and Eve are arguing. Joe says, 'Lemonade stays fizzy longer in the fridge.' Eve says, 'It doesn't make any difference.' How could you use the lime water test to find out if storing lemonade in the fridge helps to keep it fizzy?

USING CARBONATES

Activity

3 In groups:
(a) Decide how you could prove that the fizz in sherbet is carbon dioxide.
(b) Discuss why fizzy drinks rot teeth. (Teeth are made of calcium carbonate.)

Sherbet sweets have citric acid and sodium hydrogencarbonate in the middle. The acid reacts with the carbonate to make the fizz on your tongue.

Acid rain dissolves away limestone statues because limestone is calcium carbonate.

Calcium carbonate neutralises acid soil.

Figure 3 *Acids reacting with carbonates*

STARTER

Work in small groups to see how many ways you can finish these sentences.

Acids react with...

When liquids look fizzy ...

⊙ Links to other key ideas

You learned about acid reactions in Neutralisation (page 60).

ACIDS AND CARBONATES

Carbonates are common in familiar things. As well as forming our teeth, carbonates make up eggshells, limestone, chalk and marble. They **all react with acids.**

These all contain forms of sodium carbonate:

stomach tablets

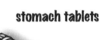

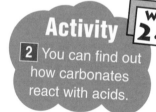

Limestone and marble are building materials. They are both forms of calcium carbonate.

Figure 2

Three things to remember about acids reacting with carbonates:

■ The carbonate starts fizzing because carbon dioxide gas is made.
■ The carbonate dissolves in the acid.
■ The acid is neutralised because carbonates are bases (they cancel out the acid).

Activity
WS **24**
2 You can find out how carbonates react with acids.

• •

REVIEW

4 Complete these sentences using words from this lesson.

(a) A _ _ _ _ react with carbonates to make c _ _ _ _ _ d _ _ _ _ _ _ gas.

(b) The fizz tells us a g _ _ is being made in the reaction.

(c) C _ _ _ _ _ d _ _ _ _ _ _ gas turns l _ _ _ w _ _ _ _ cloudy.

(d) Carbonates cancel out or n _ _ _ _ _ _ _ _ _ acids because they are bases.

5 Write a story: You are a drop of hydrochloric acid and you are dropped onto some calcium carbonate powder. What happens next? You can illustrate your story if you like. Make sure you include these words in your story:

neutralised   carbon dioxide   fizz   dissolve

COMBUSTION

AIMS

By the end of this section you should:
- **Know what is needed for combustion.**
- **Know about fire safety.**

STARTER

- In small groups, write down all the ways you can think of for putting out fires.
- Explain why each one of them works.
- Why do we think of fire as a chemical change?

FIRE!

AIR OR OXYGEN?

When iron burns, it uses up oxygen. The product formed is called iron oxide.
The <u>word equation</u> for the reaction looks like this:

Figure 2 **Iron burning in air and in oxygen**

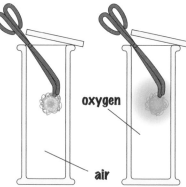

oxygen

air

Iron uses oxygen from air to burn. Iron burns **brighter and faster** in pure oxygen.

 iron + oxygen →  iron oxide

If pure oxygen replaces air in combustion, then the fire burns much hotter and faster.

Oxyacetylene welding torches burn acetylene fuel mixed with pure oxygen. The flame is so hot that it melts metal.

Activity

2 (a) Why is burning in oxygen *more hazardous* than burning in air?
(b) Write a word equation for burning magnesium.

 WS 25

Figure 3 **An oxyacetylene torch is used to weld metals together**

Figure 4 **In 1986, the spacecraft Challenger exploded when too much oxygen mixed with the burning hydrogen fuel**

Activity

3 List advantages and disadvantages of using pure oxygen, instead of air, for burning.

COMBUSTION AND OXYGEN

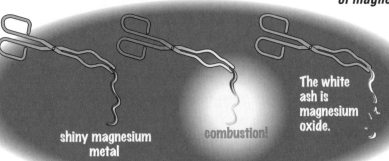

Figure 1 *The combustion of magnesium*

Combustion is the scientific word for burning.

Combustion uses up **oxygen**. The oxygen comes from the air. The products of combustion are always **oxides**. For example:

- carbon burns to make carbon dioxide
- **magnesium** burns to make **magnesium oxide**.

Remember: products are substances made in a chemical reaction.

shiny magnesium metal

combustion!

The white ash is magnesium oxide.

Activity

1 (a) How can you tell that the combustion of magnesium and carbon are chemical changes?
(b) How are the end products different from the substances you started with?

KEEPING OXYGEN OUT

To burn, fires need oxygen, fuel and heat. If the oxygen supply to a fire is cut off, the fire will go out. The things needed for fire are shown in the fire triangle. Fire services use this to put fires out.

OXYGEN FUEL HEAT

Figure 5 *Fires need oxygen, fuel and heat to keep burning*

fire blanket

Fire blankets stop clothes burning by keeping out oxygen.

Chip pan fires can be put out safely using a damp tea towel.

damp tea towel

Figure 6 *Putting out fires*

Activity

4 Explain why the damp tea towel in Figure 6 stops the fat burning. Why is a dry tea towel not used?
5 Do a survey to find out what fire safety equipment is in your lab. Use ideas from the fire triangle to discuss how the equipment works.

Follow the mouse
www.howstuffworks.com/fire.htm

REVIEW

6 Use these words to fill the gaps in the sentences.

   oxides   oxygen   combustion   products   more   less   air

The scientific word for burning is _____. Burning uses up _____ from the _____. The substances made are called _____ and are always _____.
When _____ oxygen is used, fires burn hotter and faster. When there is _____ oxygen than in air, a fire may go out.

FUELS

AIMS

By the end of this section you should:
- **Know about** fossil fuels.
- **Know what is made when fossil fuels burn.**

FOSSIL FUELS

Coal, natural gas and oil are called 'fossil fuels'.

<u>Fossil fuels</u> are usually found underground. They were formed millions of years ago from dead plants, trees and animals that were buried and pressed down by layers of mud and rocks.

We depend on fossil fuels for most of our energy needs.

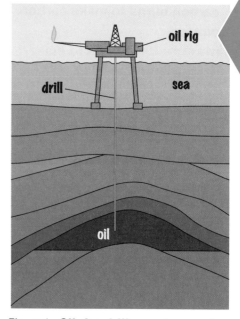

Figure 1 **Oil rigs drill very deep under layers of rock to reach oil.**

Most of the electricity we use comes from power stations that burn mainly coal and natural gas.

Petrol for cars, diesel for lorries (and even wax for candles) comes from oil.

We heat our homes and cook using natural gas.

Figure 2 **Uses of fossil fuels**

Activity

1 Discuss in a small group how you have used fossil fuels today. How do you :
- keep warm at home?
- cook breakfast?
- get to school?
- have your classroom lit and heated?

REVIEW

3 Rearrange these words and symbols to form a word equation for burning petrol.

oxygen   carbon dioxide   petrol   water   **+ + →**

4 Look at places at home where fuels are burnt, such as in a car, a boiler and in fires. Find out and write down how the waste products are taken away.

Follow the mouse
www.howstuffworks.com/fire-extinguisher.htm

BURNING METHANE

Natural gas is mainly **methane**. Figure 3 shows how we can find out what happens when methane burns.

When methane burns:

- **oxygen** is used up
- the products are **carbon dioxide** and **water**
- **energy** is given out.

This is the word equation for methane burning:

methane + oxygen → carbon dioxide + water

The **reactants** are methane and oxygen, the **products** are carbon dioxide, water and energy.

> **Remember: reactants are the substances *used up* in a reaction.**

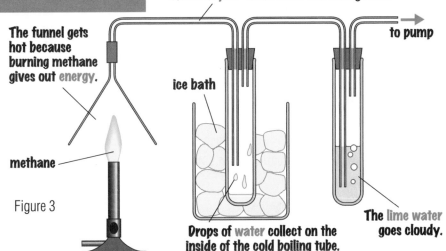

The funnel gets hot because burning methane gives out energy.

methane

Figure 3

Water vapour travels into the boiling tube.

to pump

ice bath

Drops of water collect on the inside of the cold boiling tube.

The lime water goes cloudy.

Activity

WS 26

2 (a) How does the investigation prove that carbon dioxide is made?

(b) Why can't you *see* water coming off the flame, but *can* see it collect in the boiling tube?

(c) Why does the Bunsen burner have an air hole?

GETTING RID OF WASTE PRODUCTS

When fossil fuels are burnt, there has to be a way of getting rid of the waste products that are made.

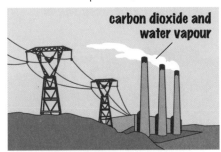

carbon dioxide and water vapour

Waste gases from power stations are sent out of tall chimneys

Carbon dioxide and water vapour go up the chimney. Waste ash is collected in the pan.

carbon dioxide and water vapour

Waste gases from central heating boilers come out through a flue.

Figure 4 *All heating fuels have waste products*

71

SOLIDS, LIQUIDS AND GASES

AIMS

By the end of this section you should:
- **Know how** solids, liquids **and** gases **behave.**
- **Know how** particles are arranged **in solids, liquids and gases.**

PARTICLES IN LIQUIDS

The scientific model that explains why liquids can pour is based on the idea that all substances are made of particles. The particles in liquids are like very, very tiny peas – so small that we can only get images of them under extremely powerful microscopes.

The particle idea is called a model because it helps us to explain how liquids behave, even though we can't normally see the particles.

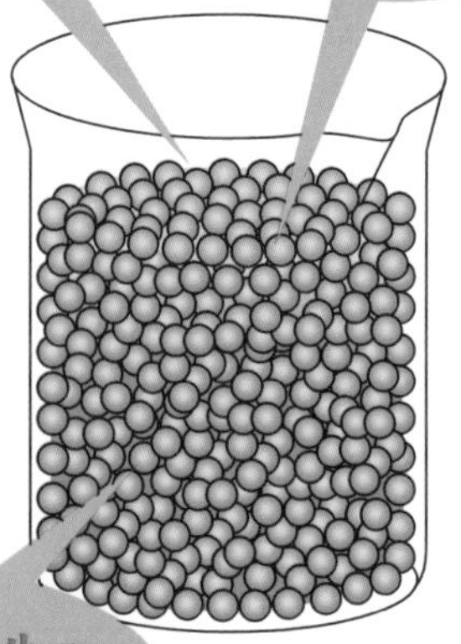

Activity

2 The **particle model** of a liquid describes the particles as being very tiny. Why is this model better than using dried peas to explain how liquids behave?

Particles of liquids settle so that their surface is flat.

The particles in liquids are far too small to see.

The particles move past each other when they pour.

The particles in liquids are very close together – they cannot be squashed to fit a smaller container.

Figure 3 *Particles in a liquid*

GASES AND SOLIDS

The particle model can be used to explain how gases and solids behave.

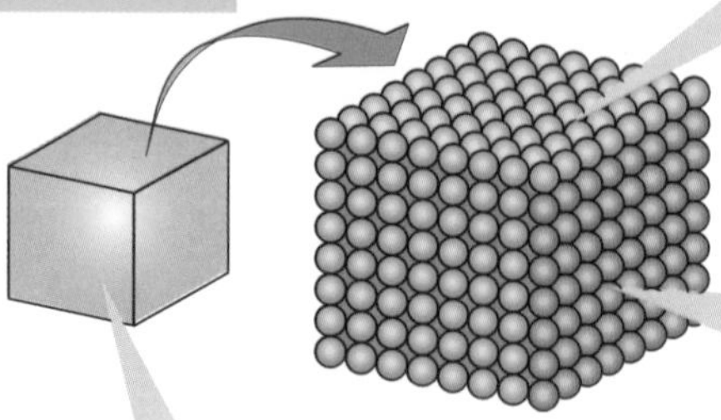

The particles in gases have lots of space between them – they can easily be squashed.

The particles move around so that gases can change shape.

The particles in a solid are all stuck together in a regular pattern.

The particles cannot move over each other – they keep their arrangement when the block is moved from place to place.

Solids are hard and cannot be squashed.

Figure 4 *Particles in solids*

Activity

3 Use the particle model to explain:
(a) why gases can be squashed but solids and liquids cannot
(b) why solids cannot change shape when they change containers.

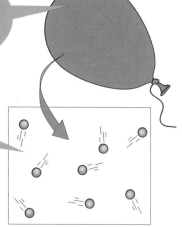

Figure 5 *Particles in gases*

STARTER

Copy the table and fill in the first row.
Write the correct form of the statements in the empty boxes.

	Solid	Liquid	Gas
Example			
can/cannot be poured			
can/cannot change shape			
is/is not hard			

POURING LIQUIDS

Liquids change shape. When orange juice is poured from one container to another, the *shape changes* so that the juice fits the new container. The surface of the orange juice is always **horizontal** (flat and level).

The orange juice is the same shape as the container.

The surface of the orange juice is flat and level.

The volume of orange juice stays the same – you can't squash orange juice into a smaller glass.

Figure 1 **Properties of liquids**

WHY DO LIQUIDS POUR?

Liquids behave like dried peas! Peas are solid, but a glass full of dried peas will pour into different shaped containers, just like orange juice.

The peas change their arrangement to fit the different shaped containers.

The number of peas stays the same.

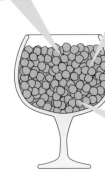

Each separate pea stays the same shape.

Figure 2 **Liquid particles are like peas**

Activity

1 A teaspoon of water changes shape when it pours on to a table.
(a) Can peas behave like this? Why not?
(b) Discuss in your group as many ways as possible for finishing these sentences.
Liquids are like dried peas because…
Liquids are not like dried peas because…

REVIEW

4 Copy this table and write 'true' or 'false' in each box.

Statement	Solids	Liquids	Gases
Change shape			
Can be squashed			
Particles are close together			
Particles are in a regular pattern			

Follow the mouse

www.schoolscience.co.uk
go to '11-14 KS3 Materials'
www.cornwallis.kent.sch.uk/intranet/elearn/
go to 'Year 7 Science Matter'

HEATING AND COOLING

AIMS

By the end of this section you should:
- Know what happens when solids, liquids and gases heat up and cool down.
- Be able to explain the changes using ideas about particles.

HOTTER AND HOTTER

The flame gives energy to the particles in the metal.

The metal turns to a liquid when the particles start moving over each other.

The liquid goes solid again when it cools and joins the metal sheets together.

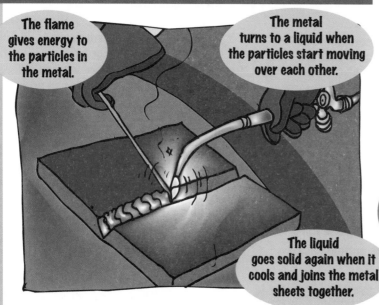

If the bar in Figure 1 gets very, very hot, the forces are not strong enough to stop the particles moving out of their places. When this happens the bar will <u>melt</u> — the particles can now move over each other and become liquid.

Figure 2 **Welders melt metals using very hot flames**

Activity

2 Draw diagrams to show what the particles look like in cold metal, hot metal and liquid metal. Label your diagrams to show which metal particles have most energy, least energy and which are in between.

CHANGING STATE

When the hot metal melts, it has changed <u>state</u> from a solid to a liquid. Melting is when a solid changes to a liquid. Look at Figure 3 for other state changes.

Three facts about **changing state**:
- The **arrangement** of particles changes.
- The way the particles **move** changes.
- The amount of **energy** particles have changes.

WS 28

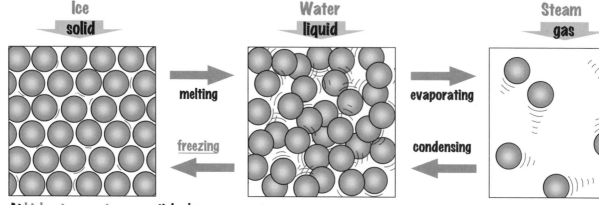

Ice
solid

melting

freezing

Water
liquid

evaporating

condensing

Steam
gas

At higher temperatures, particles have more energy and move faster, and the forces between particles are not strong enough to hold them in place.

Figure 3 **Changes of state**

∞ Links to other key ideas

You can find out more about condensing in Distillation (page 82)

STARTER

close together

lots of space between particles

Think over what you have learned about how particles are arranged. Discuss in your group which of these ideas fit particles in solids, in liquids and in gases. Some ideas fit in more than one place!

stuck firmly together

regular pattern

can move over each other

HOT METAL

Particles in solids are held together by **strong forces**. The forces act like glue to stick the particles together and stop them from moving out of their places. The particles 'jiggle about' or **vibrate** all the time.
When a solid is heated, the particles have more energy and they vibrate much more strongly. This means that when solids get hot they **expand**, as shown for metals in Figure 1.

Activity

1 Long railway lines have gaps between them so that in hot weather they don't bend out of shape and cause train crashes.
Work in pairs and draw diagrams to show why the gaps are needed. Use particles in your diagrams.

Particles in the cold metal bar vibrate.

Particles in the hot metal bar vibrate much faster and push each other apart, so that the bar expands.

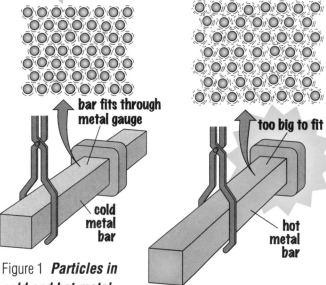

bar fits through metal gauge

cold metal bar

too big to fit

hot metal bar

Figure 1 *Particles in cold and hot metal*

Strong forces hold solid particles in place. More energy makes particles move faster.

REVIEW

3 Link the state change to the correct description.

evaporating	particles lose their pattern and move over each other
condensing	particles separate and spread out
melting	particles come much closer together
freezing	particles stop moving over each other and go into fixed places

4 A snowflake falls on to a hot car bonnet. It melts, then evaporates away. Describe what happens from the point of view of one particle in the snowflake. Use these words in your story.

more energy   faster   strong forces   vibrate   move   weaker forces   arrangement

Follow the mouse
www.cornwallis.kent.sch.uk/intranet/elearn/science/year7/matter/1page2.htm

DIFFUSION AND GAS PRESSURE

AIMS

By the end of this section you should:
- **Know how diffusion happens in liquids and gases.**
- **Know what causes gas pressure.**

GAS PRESSURE

Gas particles are moving very fast. The **force** of the particles hitting the sides of the container is called **gas pressure**.

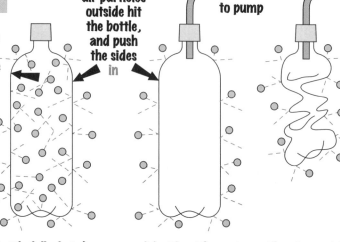

air particles hit the inside of the bottle and push the sides out

air particles outside hit the bottle, and push the sides in

to pump

A bottle full of air has the same pressure both inside and outside.

A bottle with no air has no air particles pushing out.

The air particles pushing in squash the bottle flat.

Figure 3 *Air particles hit objects with a force*

HOPPERS

Air in a space hopper gets squashed by your weight, but the air particles push back out again, making the hopper bounce back into shape. This is why balloons feel 'bouncy'.

REVIEW

3 Choose the correct words from the brackets to make this information correct.

Diffusion means the spreading out of particles. (**Gases/Liquids**) diffuse fastest because their particles move very (**slowly/quickly**). Gas pressure is caused by gas particles (**diffusing/hitting**) against the walls of containers.

4 Blow-up airbeds are comfortable to sleep on because they change shape to fit your body and feel 'bouncy'. Use ideas about particles to explain why:
  (a) airbeds can change shape
  (b) airbeds feel bouncy
  (c) airbeds go flat when you let the air out.

Follow the mouse
www.schoolscience.co.uk/content/3/physics/bama/index.htm
www.exploratorium.edu/science_explorer/watertrick.html

STARTER

- Discuss in your group why it is a good idea to compare particles to a football crowd.
- Think about how particles are *arranged* and how they *move* (you can think about *energy* and *forces between particles*, too).
- In what ways does the football crowd idea *not* compare to particles in liquids and gases?

A big crowd watching a football game behaves like particles in a **liquid**. When the spectators leave the game and scatter to go home, they are like particles in a **gas**.

DIFFUSION

Gas particles move much *faster* than liquid particles. Smells travel quickly because the 'smelly' particles move through the air (diffuse) to our noses. Particles with more energy move faster, so hot particles diffuse faster than cold particles.

Activity

1 Use ideas about particles diffusing to explain the following.

(a) Someone living next door to a fish shop can smell fish, but someone living further away cannot.

(b) There is no fishy smell when the shop is not cooking fish.

4. You smell fish when the particles reach your nose.

3. The fish oil particles diffuse (spread out) and mix with air particles.

2. The fish oil evaporates and the particles leave the fish.

air particles

1. The heat gives the particles in the fish oil more energy.

Figure 1 *Particles travel fast through the air*

Diffusion is the movement of particles when they *spread out*.

FASTER AND SLOWER

- Gases diffuse very quickly because the particles are moving very quickly.
- Liquids take longer, because the particles move less quickly.
- Most solids do not diffuse at all. Some solids diffuse very, very slowly.

Activity

2 Instructions for making a 'layer cocktail' say that the liquids must be chilled to keep the colours separate for longer.

(a) Explain why cold liquids mix more slowly than hot liquids.

(b) Choose one of the examples in Figure 2. Draw 'particle' diagrams to show what the particles look like before and after diffusion. Write a sentence about how quickly diffusion happens and why.

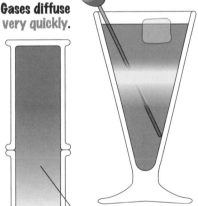

Liquids diffuse slowly. The colour takes a long time to spread out.

Gases diffuse very quickly.

Some cocktails have layers of different coloured liquids. The colours mix slowly after the cocktail is poured.

Some solids diffuse very, very slowly.

coloured crystals

bromine vapour

white jelly

Figure 2 *Particles diffuse at different rates*

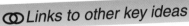

⚭ Links to other key ideas

You can find out more about dissolving in Solutions and Solubility (page 86).

SCIENCE AND HISTORY

AIMS

By the end of this section you should:
- **Know about some historical views of science.**
- **Know why scientific models change over time.**

STARTER What do scientists do?

- Work in pairs to answer this question. Try to think of as many things as possible.
- Use your answers for a class brainstorm on the board.
- What patterns can you see in your answers?

EXPLAINING HOW MODELS ARE USED

Scientists use models to *explain* what happens in the world around us. Figure 3 shows some *observations* that can be explained using the particle model.

Figure 3 *People making observations*

Activity

2 In a small group, choose a situation from Figure 3. Make a poster to show what you *observe* in your chosen illustration, and what you think is the *scientific explanation* for your observations. Your explanation should include diagrams or paper collages showing what is happening to the particles. Pair up with another group and explain your ideas to each other.

ANCIENT AND MODERN SCIENTISTS

The particle model to explain how solids, liquids and gases behave took over 2000 years to develop.

Scientists look for ideas to explain what they see. In ancient times, scientists did not have the equipment to test out their ideas, so it was very difficult for them to know if they had got it wrong!

THE GREEKS

The Greeks were great thinkers. They talked about solids, liquids and gases as being 'matter'.

All matter is made of seeds. The seeds can move in liquids and gases but not in solids.

The Moon and the Sun are carried across the sky on flying chariots pulled by flying horses.

Activity

1 Look at Figure 1 for ideas the Ancient Greeks had.
(a) What **observations** did the ideas help explain?
(b) Which ideas are not accepted now?
(c) What **evidence** do we now have to prove them wrong?

Everything contains fire. When fire is let out, it is so powerful that it destroys the matter.

Water is the basic element. All matter gives out water when we heat it.

Figure 1 *Some of the scientific views of Greeks from about 500 BC*

MODERN SCIENTISTS

Over the last few hundred years, science has changed a lot. Modern equipment and training helps us to test ideas. A scientist working today suggests a hypothesis – which is an explanation using a model – and then designs experiments to test the hypothesis. The new model is accepted by scientists if the tests support it. We accept the particle model as the explanation for matter, because it works in all the tests.

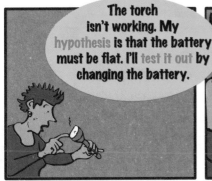

The torch isn't working. My hypothesis is that the battery must be flat. I'll test it out by changing the battery.

Hypothesis number 1 rejected! Hypothesis 2 – The bulb is broken. I'll test it out with a new bulb.

Hypothesis 2 confirmed.

WS 30

Figure 2 *Testing a hypothesis*

REVIEW

3 Finish the words in the sentences.

An ob_ _ _ _ _ t _ _ _ is what we can see happen.

A h_p_th_ _is is our idea about why something happens.

Scientists carry out many t_ _ _s before new scientific m_d_l_ are accepted.

SALT MINING

AIMS

By the end of this section you should:
- **Know how to get** pure salt from rock salt.
- **Know what salt is used for.**

MINING FOR ROCK SALT

Huge amounts of **rock salt** are found underground. The salt is from seas that evaporated millions of years ago and left the salt, sand and grit behind. The rock salt is **mined** by cutting it out of huge underground caves.

Rock salt is cut out of the ground using machinery

Rock salt is spread on icy roads and paths to stop accidents.

Rock salt is a mixture. **It contains crystals of salt mixed with sand and grit**

Salt melts snow and ice because salt **lowers the freezing point** of water – salty water stays a liquid at lower temperatures than pure water. The grit and sand also help car tyres to grip roads, and stop people from slipping.

Activity

1 (a) How could you prove that salt lowers the freezing point of water? Jot down a few sentences to outline what you would do.

(b) Find out which areas round your school are treated with rock salt in winter. Where is the rock salt stored? (Your school caretaker may be able to come to talk about it.)

Figure 1 **Mining and using rock salt**

SALT FROM ROCK SALT

When rock salt is mixed with water, the salt dissolves. We can **filter** the sand and grit, and then we can get the salt back by **evaporating** the water in the salt solution. The salt has been separated from the sand and grit. This shows that rock salt is a **mixture** of salt, sand and grit.

Dissolving

Salt **dissolves**, sand and grit do not.

Filtering

salt solution

Filter paper contains sand and grit and some salt.

Evaporating

Water evaporates and leaves pure salt behind.

Figure 4 **Getting salt from rock salt**

Activity

3 Do research to find out about the following.
(a) Why we add salt when we boil potatoes (other than for the flavour).
(b) What salt has got to do with using chlorine in swimming pools.
(c) Why people used to rub salt all over meat and into battle wounds.
(d) Why Roman soldiers called their wages a 'salary'.

WS 31

STARTER

In pairs, jot down some ideas to show how you can:
● prove that sea water is a mixture ● get sand out of sea water ● get salt out of sea water.
Join with another pair and discuss your ideas.

WHAT HAPPENS WHEN SALT DISSOLVES?

When you mix rock salt with water, the salt dissolves in the water to make a solution. The sand and grit do not dissolve (they are insoluble) and sink to the bottom.

> **Soluble** substances can **dissolve** in water. **Insoluble** substances **cannot dissolve** in water. A **solution** is made when a soluble substance dissolves in water.

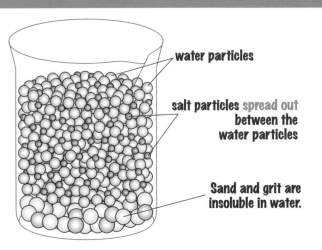

water particles

salt particles spread out between the water particles

Sand and grit are insoluble in water.

Figure 2 *Mixing rock salt and water*

THE MASS STAYS THE SAME

When salt dissolves in water, it looks as though it has 'disappeared'. But we can prove it is still there, because the overall mass stays the same.

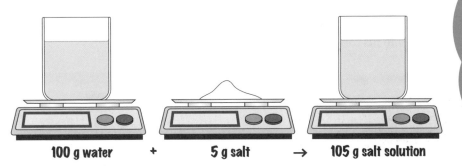

100 g water + 5 g salt → 105 g salt solution

When substances dissolve to form solutions, the mass stays the same.

Activity

2 One beaker contains pure water and another contains salty water. Work in pairs to jot down as many ways as possible you could use to tell which is which.

Follow the mouse
www.british-salt.co.uk/education/subframe.htm
www.lionsaltworkstrust.co.uk/index.htm

REVIEW

4 Match the words to the correct explanation.

soluble	does not dissolve in water
insoluble	separates a dissolved solid from a solution
solution	dissolves in water
evaporation	separates insoluble solids from liquids
filtering	a substance (e.g. salt) dissolved in water

DISTILLATION

AIMS

By the end of this section you should:
- Understand how distillation is used to get the solvent out of a solution.
- Recall some uses of distillation.

MORE ABOUT DISTILLATION

Water dissolves ink. Water is a **solvent** for ink. Distillation can be used to separate any solvent from a **solution**. The flow chart shows the processes that happen during distillation.

⊙ Links to other key ideas

You can find out more about boiling and condensing in Heating and Cooling (page 74).

The solution is heated until it boils. ➔ The solid is left behind in the flask.

⬇

The solvent evaporates and changes to a gas.

⬇

The thermometer gives a reading for the boiling point of the solvent.

⬇

The solvent gas enters the cold condenser.

⬇

The solvent gas condenses and changes back to a liquid.

⬇

The pure solvent liquid runs into the collection flask.

Activity

2 Work as a group. Make a poster-sized copy of the distillation diagram opposite. Copy each of the sentences from the flow chart onto separate pieces of paper. Stick the pieces of paper around your diagram with arrows to show where each process happens.

USING DISTILLATION

Activity

3 Distillation is an expensive process when run on a big scale because it uses a lot of fuel. Explain why a lot of fuel is needed for distillation.

Mixtures of liquids can be separated by distillation, too. Separating liquids using distillation is called **fractional distillation.**

Figure 2 **This distillation vessel separates alcohol from water for making whiskey**

Figure 3 **The fractionating column uses distillation to separate petrol from crude oil**

STARTER

Do the crossword.

1 across   A liquid _ _ _ _ _ _ _ _ _ when it turns to a gas.

2 down   A gas _ _ _ _ _ _ _ _ when it turns to a liquid.

3 down   Gas particles have more _ _ _ _ _ between them than liquid particles.

4 across   A _ _ _ _ _ _ _ _ is made when salt dissolves in water.

5 across   _ _ _ _ _ _ _ substances can dissolve in water.

CARRYING OUT A DISTILLATION

A **solution** is made when a solid dissolves in water. When a solution is boiled, the water **evaporates** to form a <u>**vapour**</u>, leaving the dissolved solid behind. <u>**Distillation**</u> is a way of cooling the water vapour so that it <u>**condenses**</u> and can be collected as a liquid. Ink and water can be separated by distillation.

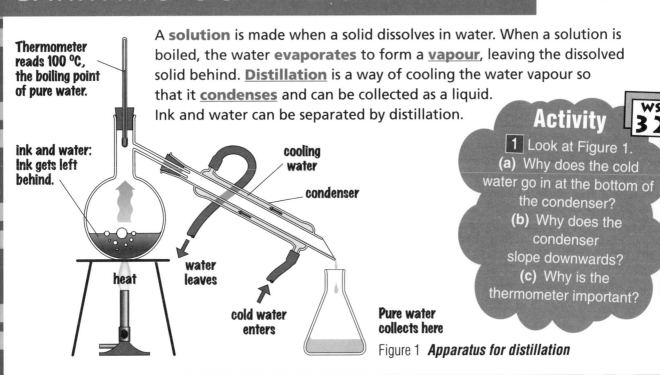

Thermometer reads 100 °C, the boiling point of pure water.

ink and water: Ink gets left behind.

heat

water leaves

cooling water

condenser

cold water enters

Pure water collects here

Figure 1 *Apparatus for distillation*

Activity

WS 32

1 Look at Figure 1.
(a) Why does the cold water go in at the bottom of the condenser?
(b) Why does the condenser slope downwards?
(c) Why is the thermometer important?

REVIEW

4 Put these sentences in the correct order to describe what happens when salt and water are distilled.

■ The thermometer reads the temperature of the steam as it enters the condenser.

■ The steam turns back into water.

■ The water evaporates.

■ Pure water drips into the collection flask.

■ The salt and water mixture is heated.

■ The salt is left behind.

■ The cold water in the condenser cools the steam.

Follow the mouse
www.epa.gov/OGWDW/kids/treat.html

5 Make a crossword using these words.

condenser   distillation   solution   solvent
evaporates   condenses   boiling point

Write the clues. See if your partner can complete it next lesson.

CHROMATOGRAPHY

AIMS

By the end of this section you should:
- **Know how to separate substances using chromatography.**
- **Understand what the spots on a chromatogram tell us.**

STARTER

Work as a class. Imagine you have three beakers each containing a clear liquid. Look at this list:

- Ink and water.   • Sugar dissolved in water.   • Pure water.

What tests could you do in your lab to find out which of these three liquids is in each of your beakers? Make a spider diagram on the board to show your ideas.

WHO FORGED THE CHEQUE? – DATA ANALYSIS

Mr Bell wrote a cheque for £30. The cheque was stolen and cashed for £3000. The thief had changed the amount on the cheque before cashing it. Mr Bell blames Mrs Carr.
He says, 'She's been short of money lately and she was here the day the cheque disappeared.'
Mrs Carr says, 'That's not true. Mr Bell wrote and cashed that cheque himself.'
The police scientist runs a chromatogram to investigate the theft.

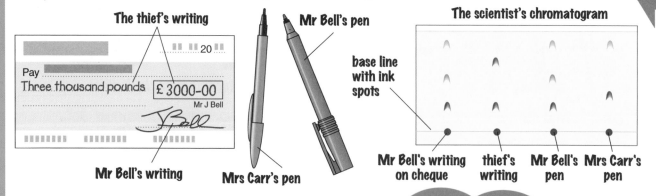

The thief's writing · Mr Bell's pen · base line with ink spots · The scientist's chromatogram

Pay ....
Three thousand pounds £ 3000-00
Mr J Bell

Mr Bell's writing · Mrs Carr's pen

Mr Bell's writing on cheque · thief's writing · Mr Bell's pen · Mrs Carr's pen

The police scientist's report

My findings:
- Ink from Mr Bell's pen signed the cheque.
- Different ink had been used to write the amount on the cheque.
- Mrs Carr's pen had not been used on the cheque.

Activity

3 Draw a sketch of the chromatogram in the centre of a sheet of paper.
(a) How many different dyes does each ink contain?
(b) Mark on your chromatogram 'least soluble dyes' and 'most soluble dyes'.
(c) Write arrows and labels to explain clearly how the results show the three findings of the police scientist. Mrs Carr is delighted. 'This proves I'm not the thief', she says. Mr Bell says, 'At least this proves I didn't change the cheque myself.'
(d) Does the report prove these two statements? Explain your view on each.

SEPARATING INKS USING CHROMATOGRAPHY

Manufacturers of felt tip pens mix dyes together to make the different colours. For example, green ink can be made by mixing yellow and blue dyes together. Felt pen ink is a solution of dyes dissolved in water. The dyes can be separated using <u>chromatography</u>.

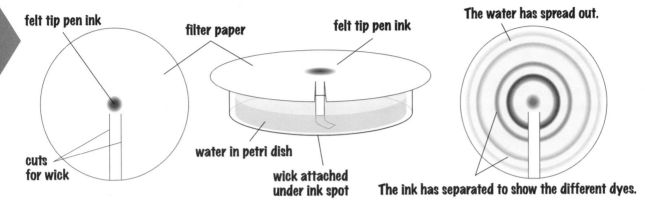

Figure 1 *Chromatograph to separate inks*

VERTICAL CHROMATOGRAPHY

Chromatography also works if the filter paper is standing up (vertical).

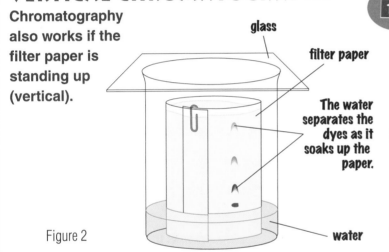

Figure 2

The water separates the dyes as it soaks up the paper.

Activity
WS 33

1 You can carry out chromatography of dyes used to colour sweets.

Activity

2 (a) Why do felt tip pens stop working if you leave their tops off?

(b) What different coloured dyes have been used in the felt tip pen ink in Figures 1 and 2?

(c) Explain why 'water soluble inks' are often used for children's pens.

WHY DO THE DYES MOVE?

The dye particles are stuck to the filter paper by forces.

The water dissolves the dyes. The dye particles 'get carried along' by the water particles (like a piggy back ride!) because the dye particles 'stick' to the water particles more strongly than they stick to the paper – the forces between dye particles and water particles are stronger.

- More soluble dyes travel further – they 'stick' better to water particles.
- Dyes that are not very soluble do not move so far.

REVIEW

4 The words in bold have had their letters scrambled. Write the sentence out so that it makes sense by unscrambling the letters.

gachtorhrampy shows what **ydes** have been used in **kin** by **arapgniset** them.

SOLUTIONS AND SOLUBILITY

AIMS

By the end of this section you should:
- **Know how to make a** saturated solution.
- **Understand what affects how much solid dissolves in a solvent.**

SOLUBILITY GRAPHS – DATA ANALYSIS

This table shows the solubilities of three substances.
Remember: solubilities are measured as the number of grams of substance that dissolve in 100 cm³ water, and solubility rises when temperature rises.

Substance	Solubility at				
	0 °C	20 °C	40 °C	60 °C	80 °C
salt (sodium chloride)	36 g	36 g	36 g	37 g	38 g
copper sulphate	14 g	21 g	29 g	40 g	55 g
oxygen gas	1.4 mg	0.9 mg	0.7 mg	0.6 mg	0.5 mg

You are going to draw line graphs on axes like those in Figure 3.
- Plot the values for salt and copper sulphate on Graph A.

Oxygen is not very soluble, so the solubility of oxygen per 100 cm³ water is given in mg (milligrams), which are thousandths of a gram: 1 mg = 1/1000 g.
- Plot the values for oxygen on Graph B.

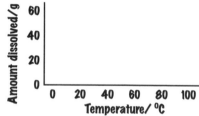
Graph A: Salt and copper sulphate

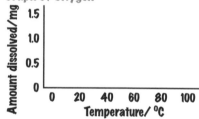
Graph B: Oxygen

Figure 3 **Solubility graphs**

Activity

WS 34

2 Look at your first graph.
(a) Which solid is *most soluble* at 20 °C?
(b) Which is *most soluble* at 80 °C?
(c) Which solid's solubility changes most at *higher temperature*?
(d) What *two* things do the data show about the pattern of *solubility of oxygen gas* compared to the solubility of the two solids?
(e) Why should goldfish owners keep their fish tanks cool?

REVIEW

3 Test your partner. Look up these words in the glossary. Read the definition (missing out the word). How many can your partner guess?

saturated solution   soluble   solubility   solute   solvent

4 Copy and complete these sentences. You can use diagrams to illustrate your answers.

Tea-bags make *stronger tea* if the water is *hotter* because…

Sugar lumps take *longer to dissolve* in tea than ordinary sugar because…

We add sugar to *hot tea* and *stir* it because…

STARTER

solvent

soluble

solution

insoluble

dissolve

Make up some sentences with these words in them to show that you understand them. See how many words you can get into one sentence. As a class, choose the best ideas and write them on the board.

SATURATED SOLUTIONS

A solution contains a solute (usually a solid) dissolved in a solvent (e.g. water).

If we add salt to water, the salt dissolves. Eventually the water becomes 'full up'. No more salt will dissolve. When this happens, we say the solution is saturated.

A saturated solution cannot dissolve any more solute.

The solubility of a solute is how much will dissolve in 100 cm³ of water.

Solubilities are measured in grams. The solubility of salt is 36 g in 100 cm³ at room temperature.

saturated salt solution

The solution is saturated because all the spaces between water particles are filled with salt.

If more salt is added to a saturated solution, it will not dissolve.

water particles   salt particles

Figure 1 *Particles in a saturated solution*

Activity

1 What is the solute and what is the solvent when:
(a) we add sugar to our tea?
(b) we take off nail varnish with nail varnish remover?
(c) Use the solubility value for salt to predict how much salt dissolves in 50 cm³ water.

∞ *Links to other key ideas*

You learned about particles in Solids, Liquids and Gases (page 72).

DISSOLVING FASTER AND DISSOLVING MORE

DISSOLVING FASTER

Dissolving can be made to happen *faster* by:
• stirring
• grinding up the solid into smaller pieces (this *increases* the *surface area* of the solid)
• using a *hot* solvent (because the *particles move more quickly*).

MAKING MORE SOLID DISSOLVE

A saturated solution can dissolve more solid if the *temperature is increased*.

A **hot** solvent **dissolves more solid** than a cold solvent.

When a hot saturated solution cools down again, we see the extra solid reappear.

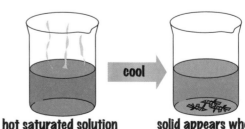

hot saturated solution

cool

solid appears when the solution cools

Figure 2 *Solubility in hot and cold solutions*

HOW ARE FUELS USEFUL?

AIMS
By the end of this section you should be able to:
• Identify some everyday fuels.
• Recall that a fuel reacts with oxygen to release energy.
• Use a thermometer to measure the temperature of a liquid.

FUELS

All fuels burn. When they burn, they use up **oxygen** and give out <u>energy</u>. The energy given out can be used for heat, light or even to make something move.

Heating a room with a coal fire.

Cooking on a gas hob.

Figure 1

Paraffin lamps are used for camping.

When the petrol in an engine burns it makes a car move.

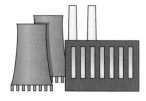
Coal is burnt in a power station to produce electricity.

Activity
1 Look at the Figure 1 diagrams. For each diagram, decide what <u>fuel</u> is being burnt and what the **energy** is being used for.

STORING AND USING ENERGY

Fuels contain energy that is stored in the chemicals in the fuel. This energy is given out when the chemicals react with oxygen and burn. This stored energy is called 'chemical energy'. Our bodies get energy to move about and keep warm from chemical energy stored in food.

Figure 2

Cars are filled with petrol. **Cars use energy from petrol to move.**

Babies eat food. **Babies use energy from food to move.**

Activity
2 Liz wrote in her science book, 'Cars and babies both use chemical energy in fuel and food for movement. They both get warm because heat energy is released at the same time. Babies use energy very differently to cars because...' Copy Liz's work and continue where she left off.

Some types of energy
Heat   Movement
Light   (sometimes
Electrical called 'kinetic')
Chemical

◐◑ Links to other key ideas
Think about the links with Fossil Fuels (pages 70 and 92).

◐◑ Links to other key ideas
Find more about how fuels release energy in Combustion (page 68) and Fuels (page 70).

Activity
3 Look at the list of types of energy. Look at the diagrams on this page. Find one example of each type of energy.

WS 36

STARTER

- Make a list of types of heaters for use at home.
- Decide whether each heater works by 'burning something' or 'not burning something'.
- Discuss whether or not you think using **electricity** to heat your home involves 'burning something'.

GETTING HOTTER

Energy from fuels is often given out as heat e.g. burning gas to heat a saucepan of water. The heat causes the <u>temperature</u> of the water to rise – we say it 'gets hotter'. We can measure temperature using a <u>thermometer</u>.

Activity

4 **(a)** What are the readings on the three thermometers?

(b) The thermometers show readings taken in boiling water, a warm room and a person's body temperature. Work out which is which.

Checklist for using a thermometer
- Keep the thermometer in the water when you take a reading.
- Turn the thermometer round until you can see the reading clearly.
- Work out carefully what each scale division means.

WS 37

Figure 3

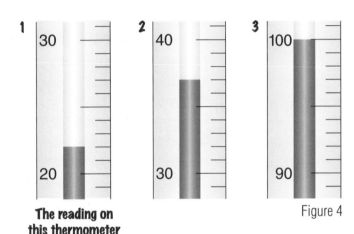

The reading on this thermometer is **22 °C**.

Figure 4

REVIEW

5 Explain whether each of the following are fuels. Remember, 'explain' means that you need to give the reasons for your answers.

Water   Gas   Electricity   Oxygen

Try to use some of the following sentence openings in your work, or think of other ways of presenting your argument clearly.

I think that water is/is not a fuel because ...

My reasons for thinking that gas is/is not a fuel are as follows. First, ...

Electricity does not ... . This means it is/is not a fuel.

All fuels ... . Therefore oxygen is/is not a fuel.

6 Draw diagrams to illustrate fuels being used to produce: **heat, light, movement.**

Follow the mouse
www.leeds.ac.uk/fuel/fuel/html
www.think-energy.com/
www.solidfuel.co.uk/
www.bp.com

THE BUNSEN BURNER

AIMS

By the end of this section you should be able to:
- **Use a Bunsen burner safely.**
- **Plan and carry out a fair test to compare the heat output of different Bunsen burner flames.**
- **Use a bar chart to compare different fuels.**

HERR BUNSEN'S WONDERFUL BURNER

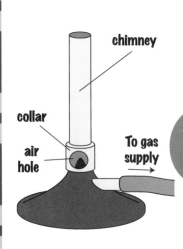

Figure 1 **A Bunsen burner**

Herr Bunsen invented the **Bunsen burner** for heating things safely in the laboratory.

Activity

1 Look at these lab rules.
- Tie back long hair.
- Keep your books and papers tidy.

Draw cartoons to show what could happen if you do not follow these rules when you use the Bunsen.

Checklist for lighting a Bunsen burner safely
- ✔ Push the tubing firmly onto the tap.
- ✔ Stand the Bunsen on a heat-proof mat.
- ✔ Close the air hole.
- ✔ Light a spill or a match at arm's length.
- ✔ Turn on the gas when you have your light ready, and light the gas.
- ✔ Move your spill or match away from the Bunsen flame, blow it out and put it on the mat.

USING THE BUNSEN TO HEAT WATER SAFELY

We often use a Bunsen burner to heat up liquids. We use a tripod and gauze to hold the beaker safely.

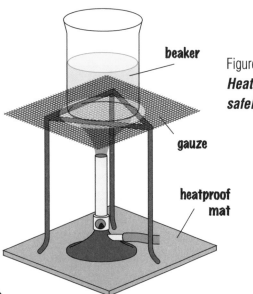

Figure 2 **Heating water safely**

Activity

2 The most common injuries from using a Bunsen are burns and scalds. Find out what to do if you burn or scald yourself. Write a 'Checklist Action Plan' to show what to do if this happens.

Checklist for heating water safely
- ✔ Don't light the Bunsen until everything else is ready.
- ✔ Never fill your beaker more than half full.
- ✔ Make sure the tripod stands firmly on the mat.
- ✔ Put the gauze and the beaker on the tripod.
- ✔ Light your Bunsen at one side.
- ✔ Open the air hole.
- ✔ Slide the Bunsen carefully under the beaker.

STARTER

Your teacher will show you how to light and use a Bunsen burner safely and how to adjust the type of flame. Working individually, complete the table.

Type of flame	Air hole
Yellow	Closed
Half blue	
Roaring with a blue cone	

ANALYSING DATA

⚭ Links to other key ideas

You can find out more about combustion and the Bunsen burner in Combustion (page 68).

The Bunsen burner uses natural gas as a fuel. Cars and other vehicles use petrol or diesel. Different fuels give different amounts of energy. The amount of energy in different fuels can be compared. The table compares how much fuel is needed by petrol and diesel cars to travel a distance of 100 km.

Type of car	Litres of fuel needed to travel 100 km	
	Petrol engine	Diesel engine
Audi A4	8.2	5.6
Ford Mondeo	7.8	6.0
Mercedes C-class	9.4	6.8
Rover 25	6.4	5.2

Patterns in the data are easier to see if it is presented as a <u>bar chart</u>. Bar charts are used to show data about different objects.

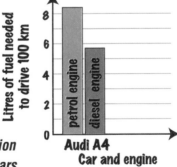

Figure 3 *Bar chart for fuel consumption in petrol and diesel cars*

Activity

3 Look at the table.

(a) Copy and complete the bar chart.

(b) In pairs, explain what this data shows about the fuel consumption of petrol and diesel cars.

(c) Look at the information and decide which fuel is a more concentrated energy source, petrol or diesel. Explain how you can tell this.

(d) Fuel such as petrol and diesel is sold by volume, not by the energy released when it burns. As a class, discuss the outcomes of this. Do you think it is right?

Figure 4 *Each litre of diesel costs about the same as a litre of petrol*

REVIEW

4 Work in pairs. One person explains how to light a Bunsen burner safely, then the other person explains how to heat a beaker of water safely. Your partner needs to check that you leave nothing out.

Follow the mouse
chemscape.santafe.cc.fl.us/chemscape/ catofp/bunsbur/bunsbur2.htm

5 Shops sell two different types of fuel for barbecues, lump wood and briquettes. Plan some experiments to find out which fuel is the best value for money. Outline what you would do and what results you would look for.

FOSSIL FUELS

AIMS

By the end of this section you should be able to:
- **Describe how fossil fuels were formed.**
- **Explain why we need to use fossil fuels less.**

FOSSIL FUELS: COAL

Fuels react with oxygen from the air and release *energy*. **Fossil fuels** are formed from the remains of plants and animals. They take millions of years to form. They are usually found buried and pressed under layers of rock that have settled on top of them. Fossil fuels include:

- **coal**
- **crude oil**; this is oil that is found below ground or under the sea bed
- **natural gas**; like mineral oil, natural gas is found in pockets under the ground or the sea bed.

Coal was formed over millions of years from plant materials that grew in swamps.

Figure 1 *Different stages in coal formation*

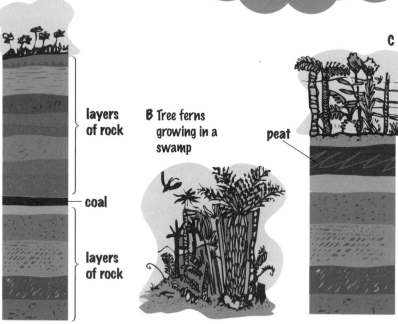

layers of rock

coal

layers of rock

B Tree ferns growing in a swamp

peat

Activity

1 The three stages in the formation of coal shown in Figure 1 are in the wrong order. In pairs:
- decide on the correct order of the diagrams
- write a description of what each diagram shows.

FOSSIL FUELS: CRUDE OIL AND NATURAL GAS

Crude oil and **natural gas** were formed from small animals and plants that lived in the sea.

⊙○ *Links to other key ideas*

You can find out more about fossil fuels in Fuels (page 70).

Activity

2 Use books, CD ROMs and the internet to find out about fossil fuels. Choose one of the following aspects to focus on:
- How they were formed
- What they are used for
- Why they are running out
- How they are mined and transported

Write a two-minute talk to give to the rest of the class. Use posters, OHTs or Powerpoint to help you make your points.

- What does the word 'fossil' make you think about? Write a list.
- What does the word 'fuel' make you think about? Write a list.
- Work in pairs to write a single sentence to explain what 'fossil fuel' means.

HOW LONG WILL FOSSIL FUELS LAST?

We are using up fossil fuels very quickly. They take millions of years to form, so we cannot replace them as fast as we are using them. This is why they are called <u>non-renewable</u> fuels. This table shows how long fossil fuels will last if we keep using them at the present rate.

Fuel	coal	mineral oil	natural gas
Number of years the known reserves will last	190	65	45

Figure 2 **Burning fossil fuels**

Activity

3 Study the table.

(a) Draw a bar chart that shows this information.

(b) Which of the following fuel-users is likely to run out of its fuel supply first? Explain your choice: diesel-powered lorries, coal-fired power stations, gas-fired power stations.

(c) What conditions are needed for coal to form?

(d) Explain why coal is not being formed at present in the UK.

Most of our fuel is used by industry to manufacture the things we use every day, and for transport. Big industrial machinery is designed to be very energy efficient, which means that working machines use as little energy as possible.

Family Action Plan
- Use less petrol e.g. use the bus not cars.
- Use less fuel for heating e.g. get double glazing.
- Use less electricity e.g. turn lights off.

Activity

4 Look at the Family Action Plan. Think of as many ways as possible that your family could cut down the amount of fuel you use every day. Talk to your family about why cutting down is so difficult. Design a sign to encourage people to turn lights off.

5 Why do you think managers of big industry are keen to use as little fuel as possible?

REVIEW

6 Give your talk about your chosen fossil fuel. Listen carefully to what the other groups have to say. Note down any questions and ask them when they have finished their talk.

Follow the mouse
www.dmm.org.uk
www.schoolscience.co.uk
www.esso.co.uk/eaff/essouk/sitemap/index/html

7 Imagine that you are living in the year 2300, when all the fossil fuels have run out. Write a diary for a typical school day. Include in your diary details of:
- how you get to and from school
- how your classroom is heated and what type of lights are used
- how your meals are cooked.

WS **38**

RENEWABLE RESOURCES

AIMS

By the end of this section you should be able to:

- **Explain the difference between a renewable and a non-renewable energy resource.**
- **Recall which energy resources are renewable.**
- **Describe how a renewable energy resource can be used to produce electricity.**
- **Understand that the Sun is the source of both renewable and non-renewable energy.**
- **Know how the Sun causes non-living things to move.**

MOVEMENT ENERGY AND ELECTRICITY

Energy from renewable resources can be converted to electrical energy. A <u>turbine</u> is a like a fan or water wheel that turns when air or water moves.

Turbines can be connected to <u>generators</u>. A generator changes the movement energy in the turbine to electrical energy that can be stored in batteries. On a large scale, the electricity can be fed into the national electricity supply through the National Grid.

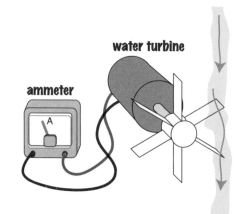

Figure 2 **Moving water produces electricity**

Activity

3 **(a)** Which renewable resources in Figure 1 can be used to turn turbines to generate electricity?
(b) Find out how turbines turn in a coal-fired power station.

A SOLAR POWERED HOUSE

<u>Solar panels</u> on the roof of a house use **solar collectors** to heat up water, or <u>solar cells</u> to convert the sunlight into electrical energy.

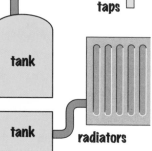

Solar collectors absorb heat from the Sun.

COLD WATER IN

taps

HOT WATER OUT

tank

tank

radiators

Activity

4 A family live in a house with solar panels. The whole family are out at work and school all day. Use the diagram to explain how the solar energy is stored so that they have a warm house, hot water and electricity in the evenings.

Figure 3 **A solar powered house**

STARTER

'We must find fuels to use instead of fossil fuels.
We can't wait until they run out to start looking because...'
Think of as many ways as possible of finishing the second sentence.

WHAT IS A RENEWABLE ENERGY RESOURCE?

Fossil fuels are **non-renewable** because they will run out. <u>Renewable</u> energy <u>resources</u> will not run out, e.g. wood is renewable because we can grow more trees. Energy from the Sun – <u>solar energy</u> – is the source of many other types of renewable energy.

Heat energy from the Sun is changed to **movement energy** when the wind blows and when rainwater flows downhill.

Other renewable energy resources
- Geothermal energy (heat from inside the Earth)
- Tidal and wave energy (energy in the movement of the sea)

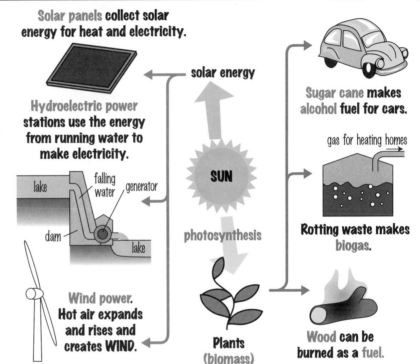

Solar panels **collect solar energy for heat and electricity.**

Hydroelectric power **stations use the energy from running water to make electricity.**

lake — falling water — generator — dam — lake

Wind power. **Hot air expands and rises and creates WIND.**

solar energy

SUN

photosynthesis

Plants (<u>biomass</u>)

Sugar cane **makes alcohol fuel for cars.**

gas for heating homes

Rotting waste makes biogas.

Wood **can be burned as a fuel.**

Figure 1
Renewable energy sources

Activity

2 Biogas can be made from cow dung. Explain why solar energy is the source of cow dung.

Activity

1 In the UK we generate some electricity from wind power and hydroelectric power. In Brazil, vast sugar cane crops are grown for making car fuel. In Spain, many houses have solar panels.
(a) Explain why these countries use different types of renewable energy. What other types of renewable energy is the UK rich in?
(b) From Figure 1, find an example of a renewable solid, liquid and gas fuel.

REVIEW

5 Explain how energy from the Sun causes these changes:
- a wood fire gives out heat
- a pebble moves downhill in a fast stream
- a wind turbine generates electricity.

Follow the mouse
www.natenergy.org.uk
www.oti.gov.uk/renewable

 6 Talk to your family about the advantages of renewable energy. Would your parents be willing to pay more for electricity if it came from renewable energy? Would they consider having their own biogas, solar or wind generator? Write a few sentences about their views.

HOW LIVING THINGS USE ENERGY

AIMS

By the end of this section you should be able to:
- Know why living things need energy from food.
- Compare the energy values of foods.
- Use energy transfer diagrams.

STARTER

Our bodies need energy from food to move about. What else does our body use energy for? What happens to people when they have less food than they need for a long time?

MEASURING ENERGY IN FOOD

Energy is stored in the chemicals in food, e.g. sugar is a food chemical that is very high in energy. Energy values in food are often shown on food labels, and are given in <u>kilojoules</u> (kJ). 1 kJ is the same as 1000 J (joules). You would use 1 <u>joule</u> of energy if you lifted a 1 kg bag of sugar by 10 cm.
Most 12-year-olds use about 2500 kJ of energy every day. If we eat food giving us more energy than we need, then we store it as fat.

ENERGY VALUES OF SNACKS

Food	Energy (kJ per 100 g)
Cheese and onion crisps	520
Apple	40
Peanuts	680
Banana	95

Activity

2 (a) Draw a bar chart to show the energy values of these snacks.

(b) Why do you think the energy values are measured per 100 g of food? Explain why this data does not clearly show how much energy there is in a bag of crisps.

(c) Eve says to Joe, 'You'll put on weight if you eat crisps every break time.' Decide what other things you would need to know about Joe before you could say whether or not Eve is right.

REVIEW

4 Make a list of all the types of energy you can think of. Explain how each type of energy can come from solar energy.

5 Look in the fridge and food cupboards.
- Make a table showing the energy values of six different foods.
- Present the information as a bar chart.
- Describe any pattern that the bar chart shows.

WS 40

Follow the mouse
www.shu.ac.uk
www.rdg.ac.uk
www.nutrition.org.uk

FOOD AND ENERGY FLOW

Our bodies need energy to grow, keep warm, for repair, to reproduce (have babies) and to move around. We get our energy from eating plants and other animals. Plants use the Sun's energy to make their own food, e.g. plants make sugar. Animals which eat plants are eating food produced using energy from the Sun.

For example, Joe eats a lamb burger before playing football. Where did the energy come from for Joe to run around?

Sun   grass   lamb   Joe

solar energy → chemical energy (in grass) → chemical energy (in lamb) → chemical energy (in Joe) → movement energy / heat energy

Figure 1

Activity

1 (a) Eve eats a boiled egg for breakfast and then walks to school. Draw a labelled diagram like the one above to show how the energy she uses came from the Sun.
(b) What do we use energy for while we are asleep?

∞ Links to other key ideas

Think about links with Food Chains (page 45).

ENERGY IN NON-LIVING THINGS

Energy changes happen in non-living things too, e.g. think about a wind turbine producing electricity to heat a house.

Activity

3 Draw a diagram to show the energy changes when the Sun makes a tree grow, then the tree is burned on a bonfire. Remember: energy is stored in wood as chemical energy.

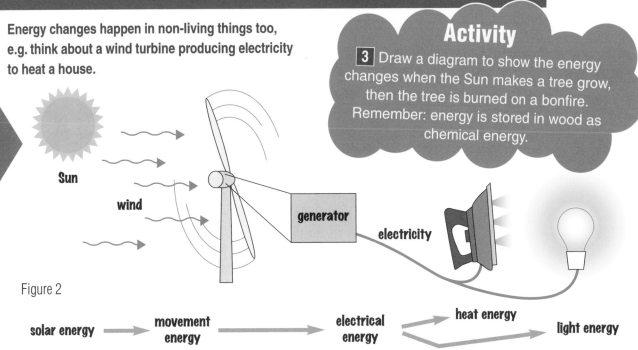

Sun

wind

generator

electricity

Figure 2

solar energy → movement energy → electrical energy → heat energy / light energy

HOW CIRCUITS WORK

AIMS

By the end of this section you should be able to:
- **Make a bulb circuit and test predictions about whether the bulb lights.**
- **Explain how a switch works.**

WHICH BULBS WILL LIGHT?

Six <u>circuits</u> are shown in Figure 1. If you are not sure about what the symbols mean, Figure 2 should remind you.

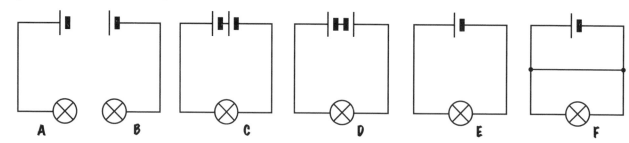

Figure 1

 bulb

 connecting wire

—|I— cell

—|I|I— battery (two or more cells connected together)

—o o— switch

Figure 2 *Circuit symbols*

Activity

1 Working in pairs, look at Figure 1.
- For each circuit, state whether the bulb will light, and give the reason for your answer.
- Use bulbs, cells and **connecting wires** to test your predictions. If your prediction was wrong, explain why.

See the complete list of circuit symbols on page 138.

REVIEW

4 Quick-fire quiz: In pairs, spend five minutes preparing answers to the following questions.
- What is the name for a number of cells connected together?
- How many connecting wires are needed to make a battery light a bulb?
- What insulator fills the gap between the connections in a switch when it is off?
- How many terminals does a battery have? What are these terminals called?
- Why can a short circuit be dangerous?

 5 Before a science lesson, a laboratory technician needs to check that all the batteries, bulbs and connecting wires have no faults. Design and draw equipment that the technician could use to check: a cell; a bulb; a connecting wire.

STARTER

- Match the names to the symbols.
- Look at the circuits drawn on the board. Which circuits will make the bulb light?

closed switch

cell

bulb

buzzer

open switch

battery

MAKING AND BREAKING A CIRCUIT

A <u>cell</u> causes an electric <u>current</u> to move around the <u>circuit</u>. This provides the energy needed to make the bulb light. A <u>battery</u> contains several cells connected together. At each end of a battery there is a <u>terminal</u> where it connects to the wires in the circuit. All parts of a circuit are <u>conductors</u> of electricity.

If there is a gap in the circuit the bulb will not light. Air in the gap does not conduct electricity. Air is an <u>insulator</u>. Plastics and wood are insulators.

A switch works by opening and closing a gap in a circuit. Figure 3 shows the switch in a torch.

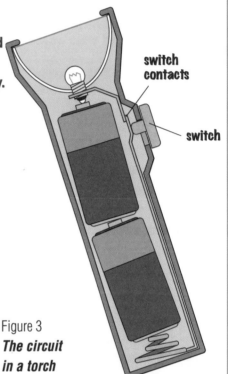

switch contacts

switch

Activity

2 Place these phrases in the correct order to describe how the torch is switched on.
- the switch contacts are pressed together
- the circuit is complete and the bulb lights
- the plastic switch slides towards the top of the torch

Figure 3
The circuit in a torch

CIRCUIT FAULTS

Why does the bulb in circuit **F** not light? There is an additional, separate wire connecting the positive and negative terminals of the cell. This is known as a <u>short circuit</u>. The bulb does not light because most of the electricity passes along the short circuit, and very little passes through the bulb.

Short circuits that form accidentally can be dangerous. The wires that make a short circuit can become very hot and cause a fire.

Activity

3 In pairs, make a list of the circuit faults that could stop a bulb from lighting.
- Make a circuit that has one of the faults you have identified.
- Swap your circuit with another pair, and find the fault in their circuit.

⬤⬤ Links to other key ideas

Think about the links with Circuits and Conductors in Key Stage 2.

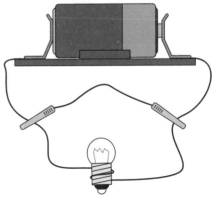

Figure 4 **The fault in this circuit is easy to spot – make yours harder to find**

WHAT HAPPENS IN CIRCUITS?

AIMS

By the end of this section you should be able to:
- **Know how components, e.g. bulbs, affect the current flow in a circuit.**
- **Know what happens when different voltages of batteries are used.**
- **Know what happens to electrical energy in circuits.**
- **Understand that components such as bulbs have resistance.**

HOW DO BATTERIES STORE ENERGY?

Electrical energy is stored in chemicals inside the battery case. Most batteries are 'dry cell' batteries, which means they contain solid chemicals. Car batteries contain concentrated sulphuric acid. When a battery is connected to a circuit, the **chemical energy** is transferred to **electrical energy** to make a current flow.

Activity

2 **(a)** Why are car batteries hazardous?
(b) Explain why 'dry cell' batteries are better than liquid-containing batteries for use in torches.

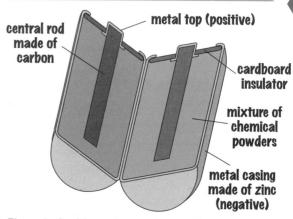

metal top (positive)

central rod made of carbon

cardboard insulator

mixture of chemical powders

metal casing made of zinc (negative)

Figure 2 *Inside a zinc-carbon cell*

CURRENT IN CIRCUITS

Figure 3

Cells make the current flow around the circuit. Components in the circuit, e.g. bulbs, resist the flow of current and use the electrical energy to make heat and light. We say that the bulb has a **resistance**. The more bulbs connected together, the *bigger* the resistance and the *smaller* the current flow.

Components such as bulbs use up the electrical energy that the current carries, but the current itself is not 'used up'. The current is the same wherever you measure it in the circuit.

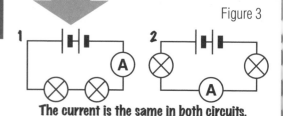

The current is the same in both circuits.

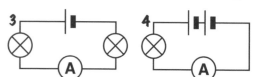

Activity

3 **(a)** Explain why the current is the same in circuits 1 and 2.
(b) Look at circuits 3, 4 and 5. Will the current be the same, more or less in each circuit compared to the first two? Explain your answer.
(c) How brightly will the bulbs glow in circuits 3, 4 and 5, compared to the first two?

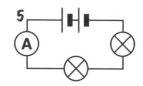

Current is measured in **amps** (A) using an **ammeter**.

—(A)—

See the complete list of circuit symbols on page 138.

STARTER

Ann is disappointed. She has put up a long line of lights in her garden attached to a battery. The lights are useless because they are too dim.

- *Think up some ideas for how Ann could make the lights shine brighter.*

CELLS, BATTERIES AND ELECTRIC CURRENT

Cells act like pumps to keep electric current flowing around a circuit. Batteries contain several cells all connected together to make a bigger 'pump'. Batteries with higher voltages are stronger pumps – they make a bigger current flow. The current transfers electrical energy around the circuit. Components, e.g. bulbs, use the electrical energy and convert it into other forms of energy e.g. movement, heat and light.

⚭ Links to other key ideas

You have met energy changes before in How are Fuels Useful? (page 88) and How Living Things Use Energy (page 96).

Activity

1 Look at the diagrams in Figure 1.
- **(a)** Write down the energy changes in a toy car and a doorbell.
- **(b)** Why do you think different voltages of battery are used?
- **(c)** Why does the doorbell use two batteries?
- **(d)** What components are in the circuits in these examples?

Cars use a 12 V battery

12V

A car transfers electrical energy into light and heat energy when it uses the battery to turn on the headlights.

electrical energy ➡ light energy and heat energy

Figure 1

9V

This toy car uses a 9 V battery

1.5V
1.5V

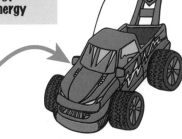
Doorbells use two 1.5 V batteries

- -

REVIEW

4 Look again at Ann's problem in the starter box. She decides to use fewer lights and to connect two batteries together. Explain, using ideas about current and energy, why her lights will glow more brightly.

5

Appliance	Batteries	Electrical energy becomes
Torch	4 × 1.5 V	light and heat

Follow the mouse
www.schoolscience.co.uk/content/3/physics/circuit

Find more examples of battery operated appliances and add them to the table.

SERIES AND PARALLEL

AIMS

By the end of this section you should be able to:
- **Know the differences between series and parallel circuits.**
- **Discuss advantages of using parallel circuits.**
- **Know some examples of where parallel circuits are used.**

SERIES AND PARALLEL CIRCUITS

When bulbs are connected in a single loop, the current has only one path to follow – this is a <u>series circuit</u>. If a bulb in a series circuit is broken, *all the other bulbs go out*, because the current cannot flow through the broken bulb.

Bulbs can also be connected so that there is more than one path.
This is a <u>parallel circuit</u>.

Key facts about parallel circuits
- They have more than one current path.
- Switches can be used to turn off one bulb at a time.
- If a bulb is broken, the others still work.

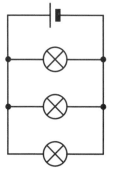

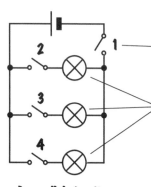

Switching off switch 1 will switch off all three bulbs.

The bulbs can be switched off one at a time using their own switches.

If one bulb is broken the other bulbs will still light.

A parallel circuit   **A parallel circuit with switches**

Figure 1 *Parallel circuits*

Activity

1 Look at the parallel circuit on the right in Figure 1.
(a) Draw the circuit and show the position of the switches when only one bulb is lit.
(b) Work out where you could put a fifth switch so that you could turn two bulbs off using only one switch.

Activity

2 Draw three bulbs and a switch in a series circuit.
(a) What happens if you turn the switch off?
(b) Write down two advantages of using parallel circuits instead of series circuits.
(c) Write a 'Key facts about series circuits' box similar to this one.

WS 43

REVIEW

4 Make a table to show the differences between parallel and series circuits.

5 Rose is putting battery operated lights in her sister's dolls' house. She wants to put bulbs in two rooms. She wants to be able to switch the lights off one at a time and have a main switch to switch them both off.
Draw a circuit diagram of a circuit she could use.

STARTER

This circuit shows one way of connecting bulbs to make Christmas tree lights.

If *one* bulb is broken, *all* the bulbs go out.

- Use ideas about current flow to explain why this happens.
- Why would this be a nuisance if it happened to Christmas tree lights?

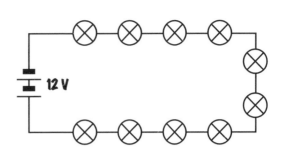

LOOKING AT BULB BRIGHTNESS

Look what happens when you use the **same battery and bulbs** to make a series and then a parallel circuit.

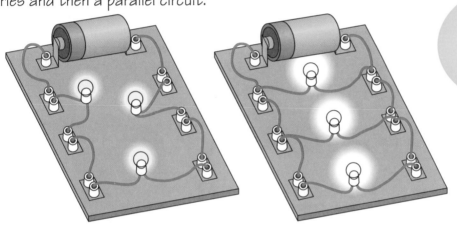

Bulbs look brighter in the parallel circuit

Figure 2 *A series and a parallel circuit*

CHRISTMAS TREE LIGHTS

Look at these two circuits for Christmas tree lights.

Figure 3

Activity

3 (a) Which circuit in Figure 3 shows bulbs connected in series? Which circuit is connected in parallel?

(b) Which would be the best circuit for tree lights? What information could go on tree light packaging to make customers buy the lights?

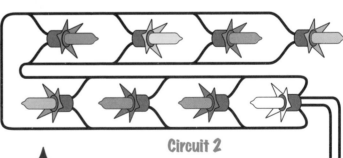

Circuit 2

to the mains

to the mains

Circuit 1

Follow the mouse

www.howstuffworks.com   search for 'Christmas lights'

www.doctronics.co.uk/circuits/htm

ENERGY AND CURRENT

AIMS

By the end of this section you should be able to:
- **Understand that the current does not get used up in a circuit.**
- **Use a model to discuss current and energy.**
- **Make predictions about current in series and parallel circuits.**

THINKING ABOUT CURRENT

SERIES CIRCUITS

We can think about current using flowing water as a model.
The bulb only lights when the current flows. The wheel only turns
when the water flows.

Figure 1 *Water behaves like current*

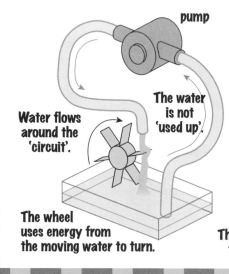
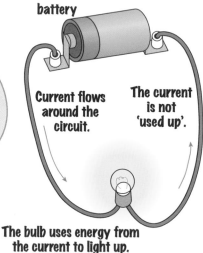

pump   battery

The water is not 'used up'.

Water flows around the 'circuit'.

The wheel uses energy from the moving water to turn.

Current flows around the circuit.

The current is not 'used up'.

The bulb uses energy from the current to light up.

Remember!
Current does not get used up when a bulb lights up. The bulb uses up the **electrical energy** carried by the current.

Activity

1 Look at Figure 1.
(a) If the water pump represents the battery, what represents the current and the bulb?
(b) How does this model help us to understand that current is not used up in circuits?

REVIEW

2 Look at the circuits in Figure 3 – they all use identical bulbs.
(a) What will be the reading on each of the ammeters in circuit 1? In circuit 2?
(b) Which circuit, 1 or 2, uses a battery with a bigger voltage? Explain your answer.
(c) Circuit 3 was set up using the same battery as used in circuit 1. What happens to the current and the brightness of the bulbs?

6A   2A

Figure 3

3 Jane says, 'A bulb acts like a turnstile at a football match. If all the people had to go through three turnstiles on the same path, the flow of people would be really slow. But if each turnstile had its own path, people could get through quite quickly.'
Use Jane's ideas to explain why the current and brightness of bulbs are different in series and parallel circuits.

STARTER

Look at this circuit.

How would the current and the bulb brightness change if you:

- connected another bulb
- moved the cell and bulbs around
- added more cells
- put another wire from A to B?

How could you measure the current in the circuit?

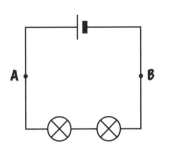

CURRENT IN CIRCUITS

Just as water can flow quickly or slowly, the flow of current in a circuit can be high or low. Bulbs have **resistance** – they oppose the flow of current and so reduce the current in a circuit.

> **We measure current in amps (A) using an ammeter.**

> ⚭ *Links to other key ideas*
> You learned about current in What Happens in Circuits (page 100).

SERIES CIRCUITS

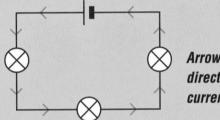

Arrows show direction of current flow.

The three bulbs are in the same path: *All three bulbs resist* the current. The current flow is *low* and the bulbs shine *dimly*.

See the complete list of circuit symbols on page 138.

PARALLEL CIRCUITS

The current has three paths to use. Each path has only *one bulb to resist* the current on each path. The current flow is *not as low*, and the bulbs shine *more brightly*.

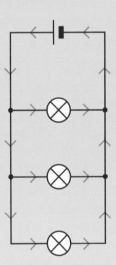

FACTS ABOUT CURRENT IN PARALLEL CIRCUITS

- The current has *more than one path* to follow.
- The same bulbs connected in parallel allow a *bigger current* to flow and shine *more brightly* than when they are connected in series.
- The currents in the branches of a parallel circuit add up to the *total current*.

A 6A (total current)

2A **A**

2A **A** — All the same!

2A **A**

2A + 2A + 2A = 6A

Figure 2

WS 44

HAZARDS OF MAINS ELECTRICITY

AIMS
By the end of this section you should be able to:
• **Describe the purpose and action of a fuse.**
• **Explain how electric currents can be harmful to the body.**

ELECTRICITY AND THE BODY

If you touch a hot object, you experience a reflex reaction which makes you pull your hand away:

• A message travels from heat-sensing cells in the hand, along a nerve to the spinal cord.
• Other messages then travel back to the arm and hand muscles.
• These messages are in the form of electric currents.

The electric currents in the nerves are normally very small, just a few thousandths of an amp, but enough to cause muscles to contract. The voltages that cause these currents are also small, a few thousandths of a volt.

Ouch – that's hot!

Figure 4 *Tiny electric currents cause the muscles to contract and pull the hand away*

Activity
3 In pairs:
(a) Describe the possible harmful effects of coming into contact with a high voltage source of electricity.
(b) Water is a good conductor of electricity at high voltages, but a poor conductor at low voltages. Explain why you are more at risk of electrocution in wet surroundings than in dry ones. Where could this happen in the home?

DEVELOPING IDEAS ABOUT ELECTRICITY

Each imaginary headline in Figure 5 refers to a real event, and each greatly helped electricity to be better understood and used.

Farmers' Weekly
Franklin Kills a Turkey

Financial Daily
VOLTA MAKES A PILE

Amphibians News
Galvani Twitches a Leg

Activity
4 Work in groups of four:
• Choose one of the headlines and find out about the event that it refers to.
• Write a newspaper article to describe the event.
• Explain in your article how it led to electricity being better understood and used.
• Prepare a 2-minute talk to give to the class.

Follow the mouse
scienceworld.wolfram.com
search for Volta, Galvani and Franklin
www.geocities.com/bioelectrochemistry/index.htm

Figure 5 *Imaginary newspaper headlines from the past*

STARTER

As a group, make a list of how accidents can happen when people are using mains electricity. What should you do if someone has an electric shock?

MAINS ELECTRICITY CAN KILL!

THE ACTION OF A FUSE

Many house fires are caused because the occupiers have fitted the wrong fuse or no fuse at all to their wiring and appliances. <u>Fuses</u> break when too much current flows through them. Too much current makes electrical wires *very hot* and *can cause fires*. Fuses prevent fires and also stop appliances getting damaged. *Every* plug should have the correct fuse fitted to it. Figure 2 shows some common fuses.

Figure 1 *Most house fires are easily avoided*

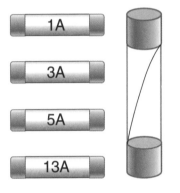

Figure 2 *Common cartridge fuses and their structure*

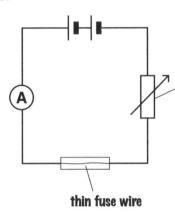

variable resistor

thin fuse wire

Figure 3 *Testing a fuse*

Activity

1 Watch the fuse wire carefully as the current in it is gradually increased.
* What happens to the fuse wire when it 'blows'?
* How does this 'break' the circuit?

CASE STUDY Ben has a bedside bulb that stays on all night. The plug is fitted with a 3 A fuse. One evening, the fuse 'blows' and the bulb stops working.
Ben doesn't have a spare fuse, so he fits a piece of thick copper wire instead. Before going to bed, he tucks the wire to the bulb under the carpet, so that he doesn't trip over it.

Activity

2 In groups of four:
* Finish writing the case study.
* Explain how Ben's actions put his life in danger.

REVIEW

5 As a group, give a talk to the class about either the case study or the historical event that you chose to research.

6 Look for labels on some appliances at home e.g. hairdryer, kettle. What fuses should be used? Ask your parents if you can look inside a plug to check it has the right fuse. Write about what you find out.

WHAT IS A FORCE?

AIMS

By the end of this section you should be able to:
- Understand the changes that forces can cause.
- Discuss forces using the words magnitude and direction.
- Measure the magnitude of forces using a forcemeter.

FORCES AND MAGNITUDE

The size of a force is called its magnitude.

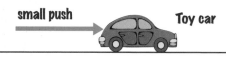

small push   Toy car

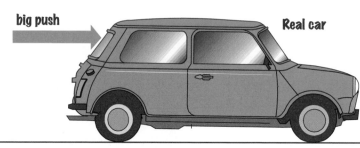

big push   Real car

Figure 2 *The force that can make a real car move has a much bigger magnitude than the force to move the toy car*

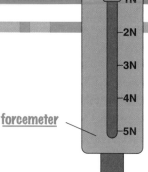

forcemeter

gravity is pulling on this 100 g apple with a force of 1 N = 1 newton

Figure 3

FORCES AND DIRECTION

Figure 4

Forces also have direction. The footballer won't score a goal if he pushes the ball the wrong way! Ben pushes a ball with a force of 50 N. What happens to the ball depends on which *direction* he pushes in – see Figure 4.

Figure 5 *The arrow shows the direction in which the dog is pulling the boy*

Activity

2 Think about these examples of forces.
- Laurie pulls a sledge through the snow.
- Alex pushes a broken down car.
- Yas sits on a cushion.
- Maddy picks up a ball from the ground.

Draw matchstick people doing these things. Draw arrows on your diagrams to show the direction of the forces. Which force has the biggest magnitude?

STARTER

Friction   **Gravity**   **Magnetism**

Force

Look at these words.
- Discuss in your groups what you know about these words.
- Make a summary on the board of the ideas from your class.

LOOKING AT FORCES

A <u>force</u> can be a **push** or a **pull**.

Got to score!

push

A. A footballer kicks a ball at a goal.

Make me go higher, Mum!

C. Pushing a swing.

Don't let me fall!

B. Saving a friend from falling.

Figure 1

What forces can do
- make a still object *move*
- *keep* an object still
- make a moving object *change direction*
- make a moving object go *faster* or *slower* or even *stop*.
- change an object's *shape*.

Activity

WS 46

1 Look at Figure 1.
(a) Are the forces in each diagram pushes or pulls?
(b) The force of the footballer's kick is making a still object (the ball) move. What are the forces in diagrams **B** and **C** doing?
(c) Draw matchstick people with arrows to show which way the forces are acting in diagrams **B** and **C**.
(d) Look at the 'What forces can do' box. Think of some examples of forces that cause each of these changes.

REVIEW

3 Finish the sentences by using these words.

forcemeter   pulls   directions   magnitude   pushes

Forces can be _____ or _____ . The size of a force is called its _____ and is measured using a _____ . Forces can act in different _____ .

4 Make a list of five forces that are involved in your journey home. Draw matchstick diagrams to show the direction of the forces and write down if you think their magnitude is 'big', 'medium' or 'small'.

FLOATING AND SINKING

AIMS

By the end of this section you should be able to:
- Understand why some objects float and others sink.
- Use ideas about balanced forces to explain floating.
- Know what the word 'upthrust' means.

STARTER

Work in groups to put forward some ideas to explain why some things sink but others float.

A penny sinks. An enormous metal ship floats.

Wood floats.

A balloon floats when it is blown up, but sinks when it isn't.

MORE ABOUT UPTHRUST

The **upthrust** of the water depends on *how much water* (the volume of water) the object pushes out of the way. Objects with *bigger volumes* push *more water* out of the way. The upthrust on bigger objects is *more* than on smaller objects. The water pushed out of the way is called the **displaced liquid**.

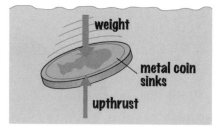
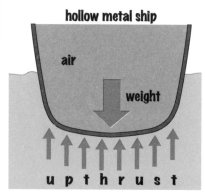

Figure 2 *The upthrust is bigger when the object is bigger*

Heavier ships 'lie low' in the water. They need to push more water out of the way because the upthrust has to be bigger to make them float.

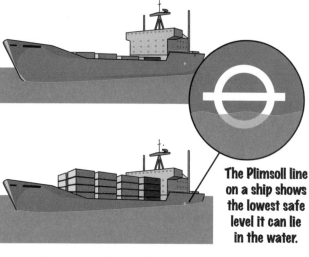

The Plimsoll line on a ship shows the lowest safe level it can lie in the water.

Figure 3 *Heavy and light ships*

Activity

2 Use diagrams showing ideas about upthrust and weight to explain why:
(a) balloons float when they are blown up, but sink when they are not.
(b) hollow metal objects e.g. ships can float, but solid metal objects sink.
(c) big ships can carry heavier loads than small ships.

3 Try to find out:
- why it is easy to float in the Dead Sea.
- what Archimedes did.

Salty water gives a bigger upthrust than pure water. It is easier to float in the sea than in a swimming pool.

GRAVITY VERSUS UPTHRUST

A plastic ball floats on water. **Gravity** is the force pulling it down. But the water is pushing it back up again. **Upthrust** is the upward force – the upthrust comes from the water pushing up. These two forces can be shown on diagrams using arrows, where the arrows show the *directions* of the forces.

forcemeter

plastic ball

Gravity pulls on the ball, giving it weight.

The water pushes the ball back up (upthrust).

Force: upthrust of water

Force: weight of ball

The forcemeter reads 0 N because the two forces cancel each other out - they are **balanced**.

Figure 1 *Forces on a floating ball*

Activity

1 A floating ball has two forces acting on it: **weight** and **upthrust**.
(a) What can you say about the **magnitude** of the two forces?
(b) What can you say about the **direction** of the two forces?

MORE BALANCED FORCES

Figure 4

When forces acting on objects are **balanced**, the forces cancel each other out and the objects:
- either *stay stationary* (do not move),
- or they *move at a constant speed*.

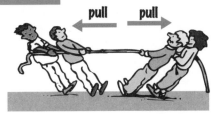

pull   pull

Forces are balanced – nobody moves.

Activity

4 Look at Figure 4.
(a) The woman is pushing the buggy. What can you say about the magnitude of her push and the magnitude of the friction pushing back?
(b) What would happen if one team in the tug of war pulled harder? Draw a diagram showing the forces as arrows to explain your answer.

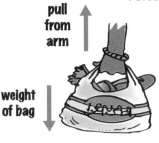

pull from arm

weight of bag

Forces are balanced - the bag does not move.

push

friction

Forces are balanced - the buggy moves at a constant speed.

5 Work in pairs to use ideas about forces and upthrust to find as many ways as possible to finish these sentences.

Objects float when...

Objects sink when...

When forces are balanced...

Follow the mouse
www.at-bristol.org.uk/explore/bermuda

CHANGING SHAPE

AIMS
By the end of this section you should be able to:
- Know how forces can change the shape of some materials.
- Know some examples and uses of elastic materials.
- Know how to improve the reliability of experimental data.

ELASTIC MATERIALS

When you apply a force to a material (e.g. by squeezing or stretching it), and then remove the force, *three* things can happen to the shape:
- The shape *does not change*.
- The shape *changes* but *returns to its original shape* e.g. a rubber band.
- the shape *changes* and *does not change back* e.g. plasticine

Elastic materials return to their original shape when you remove the force.

Rubber bands and springs can be stretched and squashed but they return to their original shape when you stop.

The wall does not change shape – the wall pushes back.

girl pushes on wall

wall pushes back

stretch!
← pull   pull →

Pastry can be rolled flat – it stays flat when you stop rolling.

Figure 1

Activity
1 **(a)** Which materials in Figure 1 are elastic? How can you tell?
(b) How can you tell that the girl leaning on the wall is an example of balanced forces?

USING SPRINGS AND RUBBER BANDS

Cars have springs connecting the wheels to the car – the springs get squashed by bumpy roads and give a smoother ride.

spring

Gates have springs to pull them shut after you open them.

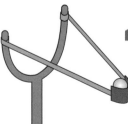

Catapults throw missiles using rubber bands.

Figure 2

Activity
2 Choose *one* of the drawings in Figure 2. Draw labelled diagrams to show how the shape of the spring or rubber band changes when it is used.

STARTER

Look at these materials: How do they change when you push and pull them? Which go back to their original shape?

plasticine

sponge

MEASURING THE EXTENSION OF A SPRING

Kim did an experiment to find out how much a spring stretches (its <u>extension</u>) when she pulled it with a forcemeter. She tested two different springs.

Figure 3 **Kim's experiment and results**

MAKING RESULTS RELIABLE

<u>Reliable</u> results are results that we are very confident about. They are **accurate** and **repeatable** – they stay the same if someone else repeats the experiment.

We can make results more reliable by:

- repeating readings and taking averages.
- drawing graphs – this makes it easier to spot 'wrong' results.
- repeating readings if they do not seem to fit a pattern.

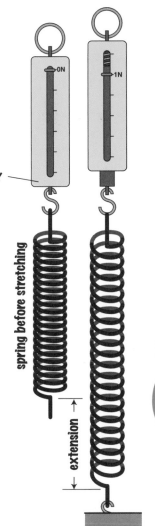

forcemeter

spring before stretching

extension

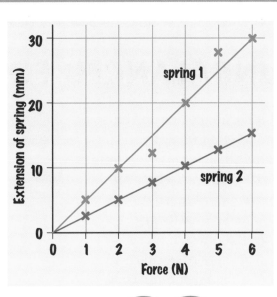

Activity

3 **(a)** Which of Kim's springs stretches most easily? Explain how you can tell.

(b) Which results do you think Kim should re-check? Explain why.

(c) Kim writes in her book, 'The results for spring 2 are more reliable than for spring 1'. Why do you think she thinks this? What can she do to make her results more reliable?

(d) Predict what the extension for each spring will be for a force of 8 N. Explain your answer.

REVIEW

4 Work in pairs. One person describes one of these words while the other has to guess which word it is. Take turns until you have guessed all the words.

spring   elastic material   extension   reliable   forcemeter   newton

5 Find something at home that works using batteries. Open the battery compartment and find out why a battery needs a spring to work. Draw a diagram to show what you have found out.

BALANCED AND UNBALANCED FORCES

AIMS

By the end of this section you should be able to:
- **Know about forces on objects moving at constant speed.**
- **Predict what will happen when forces are unbalanced.**
- **Explain how and why the speed and direction of moving objects change.**

UNBALANCED FORCES

If a ball is resting on the ground and we apply a force to it, for example by kicking it, it will **start to move**. Unbalanced forces can make **stationary objects move**.

If a ball is already moving and we apply a force to it, the movement will change because the forces are unbalanced.

Unbalanced forces can make **moving objects**:
- change speed – go **faster** or **slower** or even **stop moving**
- change **direction**.

Force on moving ball	What happens?
	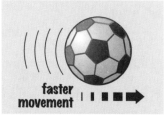 faster movement
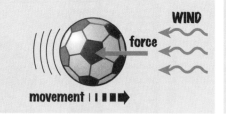	 slower movement
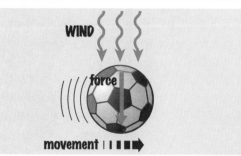	 movement changes direction

Activity

3 (a) What three changes can happen if a force acts on a ball in the opposite direction to its movement?

(b) Put the three changes in the order 'caused by biggest force' to 'caused by smallest force'.

Activity

4 Draw some 'matchstick person' cartoons showing someone playing with a moving ball. Draw some arrows on the cartoons to show how your person could make the movement of the ball change in different ways.

STARTER

Sue is skating across an ice rink at a fixed or constant speed. List as many ways as possible that her movement could change. What direction would a force need to act on Sue to cause each change?

BALANCED FORCES

When forces are balanced, objects either *stay stationary* or *move with a constant* _speed_.

Figure 1

Martyn and his dog are pulling with the same force – no movement.

Martyn and his dog are pulling with the same force – they are moving at a constant speed.

If Martyn gives a big pull, the forces are unbalanced and the dog will suddenly move faster.

⚭ *Links to other key ideas*

You learned about other balanced forces in Floating and Sinking (page 110).

USING FORCEMETERS

We can measure the forces acting in a 'tug of war' using forcemeters.

Figure 2

Unbalanced forces: the object moves to the left   Balanced forces: they result in no movement

Force to left in N	Force to right in N	Movement of rope
7	3	
5.5		to right
6	6	
	2.5	to left

Figure 3 *Forcemeters used in tug-of-war*

Activity

1 Copy the table and fill in the blanks by making predictions.

2 Look at the drawings of Martyn and the dog in Figure 1. Draw a sketch to show the sizes of the pulls when Martyn first made his dog move.

REVIEW

5 Make a table using the headings 'Balanced forces' and 'Unbalanced forces'. Write notes in each column to show what you have learned.

Follow the mouse
www.learner.org/exhibits/parkphysics/coaster

MASS, WEIGHT AND FRICTION

AIMS

By the end of this section you should be able to:
- **Know the difference between mass and weight.**
- **Know how friction acts on stationary and moving objects.**
- **Know where friction is helpful and unhelpful.**
- **Suggest ways of reducing friction.**

MASS AND WEIGHT

The **mass** of an object is how much 'stuff' is in the object – a pile of books contains more 'stuff' than one book. The **weight** of an object is the size of the force pulling it downwards – a pile of books has more weight than one book. Weight is caused by **gravity** pulling down on the mass of the object.

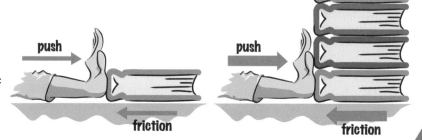

Figure 4 *It is easier to push one book across a desk than a whole pile. One book has much less weight. The frictional force is bigger when the weight is bigger*

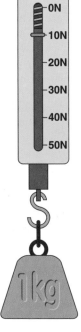

forcemeter

0N
10N
20N
30N
40N
50N

1kg

Figure 5 *A 1 kg mass has a weight of 10 N on the Earth*

If you went to the Moon you would weigh less because the Moon has a smaller gravitational pull, but you would not be any thinner! Your mass would still be the same.

∞ Links to other key ideas

You learned about upthrust and weight changes in Floating and Sinking (page 110).

Changing frictional forces

Friction can be made **smaller** by:
- using **lubricants**, e.g. putting oil on machinery.
- making surfaces **smoother**, e.g. playground slides.

Friction can be made **bigger** by:
- making surfaces **rough**, e.g. putting treads on car tyres.
- using **gritty** materials, e.g. using rock salt and grit on icy roads.

Activity

3 Use ideas about friction and weight to explain why:
(a) toddlers slip on ice more easily than grown-ups.
(b) sledges do not move as easily if more people climb on.
(c) the bottom of swimming pools need to be very rough to stop you from slipping.

STARTER

Think about these activities.
Sort the activities out into 'friction helpful' and 'friction unhelpful'. What would happen if there was no friction in each activity? What would happen if there was very high friction?

striking a match

skating

using a playground slide

climbing a rope

turning a key in a lock

stopping a car

WHAT DOES FRICTION DO?

Figure 1

<u>Friction</u> is a force that stops slipping and sliding. **Rough surfaces**, e.g. sandpaper, have *bigger frictional forces* than smooth surfaces, e.g. ice. Friction can *stop things moving* or *slow things down*.

Friction between the gymnast's hands and feet and the rope stop her from falling.

The parachutist falls at constant speed because friction between the air and the parachute pushes up against his weight.

Rusty engines do not work – there is too much friction to allow the parts to move.

Friction is needed for things to *start moving*.

grip

slip

Figure 2

Other facts about friction
Friction between surfaces:
* makes *heat*, e.g. rubbing your hands together, striking a match.
* *wears the surface away*, e.g. the heels of your shoes.

dry road   wheel turning

patch of ice

grip

skid

Figure 3 *Cars skid on ice and oil because the wheels cannot grip the road*

Activity

1 (a) Look at the gymnast and parachutist in Figure 1. Are the forces balanced or unbalanced in each diagram? How can you tell?
(b) Why should the gymnast holding the rope put lots of powder (talc) on her hands?

2 Use ideas about friction and unbalanced forces to explain why it is so difficult to walk on ice. Draw diagrams to help you.

REVIEW

4 Work in groups of two pairs. Write a two-minute talk about friction. Draw some sketches to help you make your points. Each pair chooses one of the following opening phrases:
either 'We depend on friction for our lives because...'
or 'Friction is a nuisance because...'
Take turns to give your talk to each other.

WS 50

5 Look at a bike. Find out where friction is useful and where it is not. How is friction made smaller on the moving parts of bikes?

Follow the mouse
www.exploratorium.edu/cycling
www.exploratorium.edu/hockey
www.exploratorium.edu/ronh/weight

STOPPING DISTANCES

AIMS

After studying this section you should be able to:
- **Describe the relationship between the stopping distance of a vehicle and its speed.**
- **Explain how factors other than speed can affect the stopping distance of a vehicle.**

FRICTION AND STOPPING

Friction is a nuisance to people who are sledging or skiing. It slows them down and limits their top speed.
But friction is essential to a cyclist. Without friction, the cyclist cannot get going, change direction, or even stop! When a cyclist applies the brakes:

- friction between the brake blocks and the wheel rims slows the wheels down
- friction between the road surface and the tyres prevents the bike from sliding.

Light beams can be used to accurately measure speed and stopping distances of toy cars. Road safety can be improved if we understand what affects how quickly cars stop.

friction   friction

Figure 1

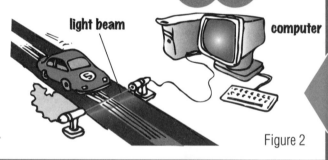

light beam   computer

Figure 2

Activity

1 **(a)** In pairs, draw a diagram that shows the friction force between the wheel of a bicycle that is braking and the road surface.
(b) Describe how this is different from the friction force that acts when the bike is setting off.
(c) Explain what happens when a bicycle 'skids'.

THE HIGHWAY CODE

All drivers have to follow the rules of the Highway Code. This is a table of stopping distances from the Highway Code. The table shows how far a car travels after the driver sees a hazard in the road.

To work out the **total stopping distance**, add the **thinking distance** to the **braking distance**:

e.g. at 30 mph, the total stopping distance = 9 m + 14 m = 23 m.

Speed of car in miles per hour (and metres per second)	Driver's thinking distance (m)	Braking distance (m)
20 (9 m/s)	6	6
30 (13 m/s)	9	14
40 (18 m/s)	12	24
50 (22 m/s)	15	38
60 (26 m/s)	18	55
70 (30 m/s)	21	75

Activity

2 Why is there a 'thinking distance' before the driver presses the brake?
3 **(a)** Work out the total stopping distance at each speed.
(b) Draw a line graph of stopping distance, in metres, against speed, in metres per second.
(c) Write a couple of sentences to say what your graph shows.

STARTER

Tom and Jack are going fast on their bike when a toddler runs into the road in front of them. Tom puts the brakes on quickly.

- Make a list of as many things as possible that will affect how far the bike will go before it stops.
- Use ideas about friction to explain your views to your group.

STOPPING FOR REAL

There is always a time delay between seeing a hazard and applying the brakes. The distance travelled during this time is the 'thinking distance' and is shown in blue in the Highway Code. To allow enough room for a vehicle to stop safely, this distance also has to be taken into account.

Tyres, weight and road surface can also affect the stopping distance of a vehicle.

TYRES

In wet weather, water passes through the tread so that the tyre stays in contact with the road.

Figure 3 *Tyres have grooves in them called tread*

WEIGHT

Cars sometimes have a greater load than at other times.

Figure 4 *A fully loaded people carrier*

ROAD SURFACE

High-friction surfaces are often applied to the road surface at roundabouts.

Figure 5 *The road surface is rougher at roundabouts where traffic needs to slow down*

Activity

4 In groups of four to six:
- use books, CD-ROM or the internet to find out and explain how tyres, weight and road surface affects braking distance
- present your findings as a short report
- prepare a two-minute talk to give to the rest of the class at the end of the lesson.

REVIEW

5 Adverts can encourage drivers to drive more safely. One says 'Kill your speed, not a child'. In your group, think about what drivers need to do to stop safely. Write some slogans for adverts.

6 The speed limit for vehicles where there are houses is 30 mph (13 m/s). Some people think this should be changed to 20 mph (9 m/s). Explain how effective you think this would be in:
(a) stopping accidents
(b) reducing the number of people injured in accidents.

Follow the mouse
www.highwaycode.gov.uk

WS 51

DAYS, MONTHS AND YEARS

AIMS

By the end of this section you should be able to:
- **Make a model that shows the relative positions of the Earth, Moon and Sun.**
- **Explain how the movement of the Earth causes daily and annual changes.**
- **Describe how the month is based on the movement of the Moon.**

STARTER

A Earth   **C Sun**   **B Moon**

Place these in order of size, starting with the largest and ending with the smallest. Write the letters in the correct order on a whiteboard or sheet of white paper. Hold it up when your teacher tells you.

A YEAR IN TIME

There are ways you can tell when it will be precisely a year from now.

Activity

6 As a class, discuss what changes take place in one year: **(a)** on Earth, **(b)** in the sky. Do similar changes take place on other planets?
Use the whole classroom to make a model of the Earth's movement around the Sun, including the Earth's spin. Check that your model explains the changes over a year that you discussed.

THE MOON AND A MONTH

MOVEMENT OF THE MOON

The Moon is not always visible in the night sky, and when it is visible, usually less than half of it can be seen. When the whole of one side of the Moon is visible it is called a 'full Moon'.

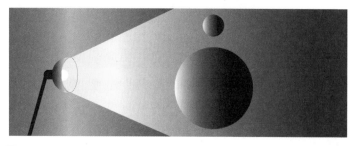

Figure 2 *A model of the movement of the Earth and the Moon relative to the Sun*

Activity

7 Work in groups of four.
- Make a model that shows the positions of the Earth, Moon and Sun when the whole of one side of the Moon is visible from the UK.
- Use a diary or calendar to find how often a full Moon occurs.
- Use this information to describe the movement of the Moon.

Activity

8 Why was the appearance of the Moon in the sky important to people who lived thousands of years ago, before the calendar and clocks were invented?

A MONTH

It takes the Moon twenty-seven and a half days to travel once around the Earth, but a full Moon occurs only every twenty-nine and a half days. This is because, at each monthly interval, the Sun, Earth and Moon are in slightly different positions in the sky.

We now use calendar months, but the length of a month used to be based on the appearance of the Moon, and we still talk about a lunar month.

DAY AND NIGHT: MOVEMENT OF THE EARTH, SUN AND MOON

MODELLING THE SUN, EARTH AND MOON

A tennis ball, a football and a bulb can be used to make a model of the <u>Sun</u>, Earth and Moon.

Activity

1 In pairs, choose the small object you think best to represent each large body. Write each choice in a table, adding the reason for your choice.
Which small object is not a very good model of the large body that it represents? Explain why. Keep your equipment for Activity 4.

Activity

2 In groups of four, use a model like this to show:
- how day becomes night and night becomes day
- at which part of the planet it is daybreak and at which part it is dusk. Demonstrate your model to another group and examine their model.

DAY AND NIGHT

As in Figure 1, a bulb and a ball can show that, at any time, half of a planet is lit up by the Sun.

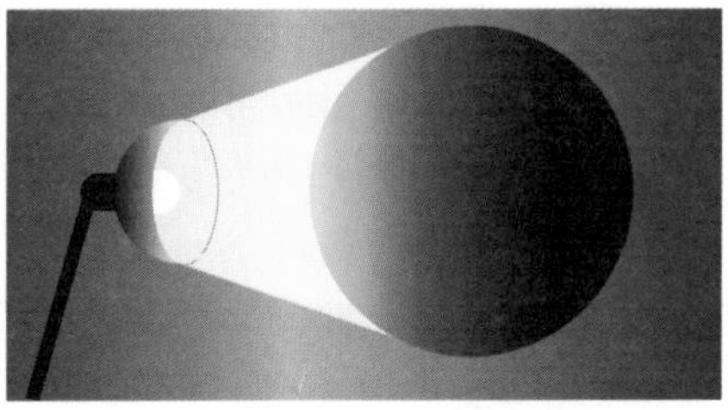

Figure 1

DOES THE SUN OR THE EARTH MOVE?

If you are seated in a fast-moving car or train, it seems as if the countryside is hurtling past you. Yet you are moving and the countryside is staying still.
Although the Earth is spinning round, we are not aware that the ground under our feet is moving. It seems to us to be still, and that the bodies in the sky are doing all the moving. The Activity 1 model can show why and how the Sun appears to move across the sky.

Activity

3 Use the words 'axis', 'day', 'pole' and 'spin' to explain how the Earth's movement causes night and day. Check your explanation by looking at a model of the Earth's movement on video or CD-ROM.

Activity

4 In groups of four, stick a 1 cm high plasticine person in the northern hemisphere of your Earth. Rotate the Earth slowly. As the Earth turns round, note the changes in:
- the person's shadow
- the direction the person has to look to see the Sun.
Show your model to another group and examine theirs.

Activity

5 On a diagram, draw the person's shadow and the Sun as he sees it in the sky, looking south towards the equator, at various times between sunrise and sunset.

REVIEW

9 As a class and on the board:
- summarise how measurements of a day, a month and a year are based on the movement of the Earth, Moon and Sun
- explain why the movement of the Sun and the Moon seems to be different when viewed from the Earth and from space.

Follow the mouse
bbc.co.uk/science/space/solarsystem/

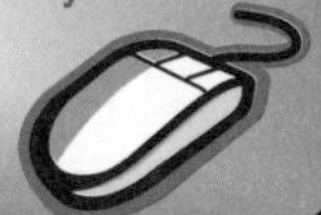

10 Imagine that you are far above the Sun, looking down on the Earth's North Pole.
(a) Draw a diagram that shows the Earth's orbit around the Sun.
(b) Draw a cross to mark the position of the UK on the Earth.
(c) Explain how the Earth's movement causes sunrise and sunset in the UK.
(d) Explain how sunrise and sunset times differ in Australia, on the far side of the Earth.
(e) Describe how you would convince a younger brother, sister or cousin that sunrise and sunset are caused by movement of the Earth and not by movement of the Sun.

SEEING INTO SPACE

AIMS

By the end of this section you should be able to:
- **Describe how stars, planets and moons are seen from the Earth.**
- **Explain why the appearance of the Moon changes.**
- **Describe the events that cause an eclipse.**

STARTER

The photograph shows an astronaut's view of the Earth. As a class, discuss the answers to these questions:

- Why does the Earth look mostly blue?
- Why does the astronaut not see the whole of one side of the Earth?
- Whereabouts is the Sun? How can you tell?

OBJECTS IN SPACE THAT TRANSMIT AND REFLECT LIGHT

Activity

1 Why do the Sun and other stars seem to be very small objects in the sky?

<u>Stars</u> are very hot objects that transmit light. Some are getting hotter, and some are cooling down. Stars are the sources of all the light in the sky. All other objects reflect light from the stars.

<u>Planets</u> and <u>moons</u> reflect light in the same way that the rock does – in all directions as Figure 2 shows. So you do not have to be in a particular position to be able to see the Moon. At the same time, from different positions on Earth, you get slightly different views.

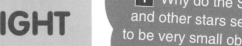

mirror   rock

Figure 1

Activity

2 In pairs, shine torchlight at a mirror and a rock. Sketch how the mirror and the rock reflect the light differently. Look at the mirror from several positions. Can you always see the torch beam? Complete the sentence using 'scatters' and 'reflects': The mirror … the beam of light in one direction only, but the rock … the light in all directions.

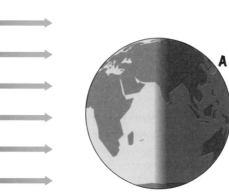
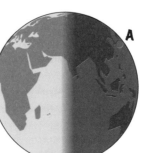

Moon

light from Sun   Earth

A

Figure 2

Activity

3 Dan is standing at A. Explain where the light comes from that allows Dan to see the Moon. Use these words in your answer: rock   transmits   reflects   Moon   Sun   light   eye

PHASES AND ECLIPSE OF THE MOON

PHASES OF THE MOON

The appearance of the Moon changes on a monthly cycle.
The changes are because:

* at any one time, only half of the Moon is in sunlight
* not all of the lit half of the Moon may be visible from the Earth.

Phase 1

Figure 3 *Two phases of the Moon*

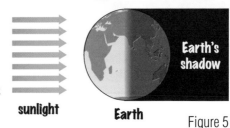

Figure 4 *Some phases of the Moon, not in the correct order*

Activity

4 Draw diagrams showing the phases of the Moon in the correct order.

ECLIPSE OF THE MOON

Light travels in straight lines, and the Sun lights up just the half of the Earth that faces it. The half away from the Sun is in shadow.
The Earth casts a large shadow and the Moon is a smaller body. When the Earth comes between the Sun and the Moon, the Moon falls completely into the Earth shadow and cannot be seen. This is an <u>eclipse of the Moon</u> and occurs quite frequently somewhere in the world.

Activity

5 In pairs, look at Figures 2 and 5 and work out why you can never see a completely Full Moon.

sunlight   Earth   Earth's shadow

Figure 5

ECLIPSE OF THE SUN

We see an <u>eclipse of the Sun</u> when:

* the Moon passes between the Sun and the Earth
* the Moon casts a shadow that moves across the Earth.

Although the Moon is much smaller than the Sun, it is just the right size and distance from the Earth to block out the Sun completely when it passes between them. This happens more rarely than eclipses of the Moon.

* We see a **partial eclipse** at places where the Moon covers part of the Sun.
* We see a **total eclipse** where the Moon covers all of the Sun.

Activity

6 In pairs, use a bulb, a tennis ball and a table tennis ball to make models that show:

* an eclipse of the Moon
* a total eclipse of the Sun.

Draw diagrams to show how these eclipses occur.

REVIEW

7 Work in pairs using sources such as books, CD-ROMs and the internet to find out:
* how often eclipses of the Moon occur
* why the Moon's orbit prevents an eclipse of the Moon from occurring each month. Prepare a brief report and present it to the class.

8 Imagine that an eclipse of the Sun is about to happen. Your part of the Earth will be plunged into a darkness like dusk. You are one of thousands of people who have gathered together to witness the event. Write an account of your experiences before, during and after the eclipse.

Follow the mouse
www.nmsi.ac.uk/eclipse/eclipselab/

SEASONS AND THE INNER PLANETS

AIMS

By the end of this section you should be able to:
- **Explain how the Earth's tilt causes variations in hours of daylight and temperature.**
- **Use temperature sensors to compare the effect of the Sun at different points on the surface of the Earth.**
- **Use data about other planets to compare their conditions to those on the Earth.**

DO THE INNER PLANETS HAVE SEASONS?

The seasons are due to the Earth's tilt on its axis. Tilt affects the number of hours of daylight for different places on Earth. The time of spin determines day length. Both tilt and time of spin influence temperature. The four inner planets, those whose orbits lie between the Sun and the asteroid belt, are the warmest planets. The table gives some information about them.

Planet	Average distance from Sun compared to Earth	Time taken to spin on axis in Earth days	Angle of axis tilt	Surface temperature
Mercury	0.4	59	7°	varies from very cold to very hot
Venus	0.7	243	2.5°	very hot all the time
Earth	1.0	1	23°	warm
Mars	1.5	1	24°	varies from cold to warm

Activity

2 In groups of four, answer the questions. Prepare to report to the class later.
(a) Which planet may have seasonal variations like those on Earth? Explain your answer.
(b) Explain whether information in the table supports answer **(a)**.
(c) What other information do you need to be more certain about your answer?

Activity

3 In groups of four, answer these questions.
(a) What causes the large variation of temperature on Mercury?
(b) Explain why there is very little seasonal variation in temperature on Venus.
(c) What is unusual about the temperature on Venus, and why is it unusual?

A HOLIDAY ON MARS

Are we nearly there yet?

I feel space sick.

Of all the planets, Mars is closest to Earth in its surface conditions:
- Days and nights are of similar length to those on Earth.
- The maximum daytime temperature is similar to Earth's, but the nights are much colder
- There may be frozen water below the surface of Mars.

Unlike the Earth,
- Mars has very little atmosphere
- its atmosphere is composed mainly of carbon dioxide
- its thin atmosphere allows a lot of the Sun's ultraviolet radiation to reach its surface.

Activity

4 In groups of four, prepare a leaflet that encourages people to take their holidays on Mars. Your leaflet should emphasise the benefits of holidaying on Mars, but also make people aware of the steps they need to take to cope with the different conditions.

STARTER

What are the differences between spring, summer, autumn and winter? As a class, make a list of the characteristics of each season on the board. Discuss the answers to these questions:

- Do all parts of the Earth's surface go through a similar pattern of change during the course of a year?
- What causes the seasons?
- Are there seasons on other planets?

THE EARTH'S TILT: SUMMER AND WINTER

If the Earth's spin was in the same plane as its <u>orbit</u> (so they could be drawn on a flat sheet of paper) there would not be seasons.

As the Earth moves in its orbit around the Sun:
- it spins round an axis through its poles
- its axis is tilted
- this axis always points in the same direction – towards the star Polaris or Pole Star.

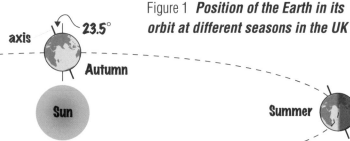

Figure 1 **Position of the Earth in its orbit at different seasons in the UK**

axis 23.5°

Autumn

Winter

Sun

Summer

Spring

Activity

1 Use a large globe and a bulb in a dark room. Place the globe so that it is the middle of summer in the northern hemisphere, and rotate it slowly on its axis.
Describe how much time during one day there is sunlight: **(a)** at the North Pole, **(b)** at the South Pole, **(c)** in the UK.

No matter how sunny a day it is in winter, the Sun does not feel as warm as it does in summer.
Figure 2 shows how the Earth's tilt explains this:
- In summer the northern hemisphere is tilted towards the Sun.

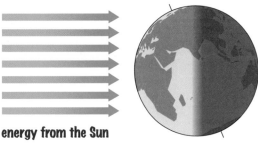

energy from the Sun

Figure 2 **Summer in the northern hemisphere**

- Energy from the Sun is spread out over a smaller area than it is in winter
- The smaller the area that the energy is spread over, the greater the heating effect it has.

REVIEW

5 As a class, summarise the causes of seasons on the board.

6 Give group reports and discuss answers to Activities 2 and 3.

7 Look again at Activity 1 and predict the answers to the questions when it is winter in the northern hemisphere. Use the globe and bulb to test your predictions.

8 Draw a scale diagram showing the Sun and the orbits of the four inner planets.

Follow the mouse
bbc.co.uk/science/space/solarsystem/

THE SOLAR SYSTEM

AIMS

By the end of this section you should be able to:
- **Describe the different types of object that make up the Solar System.**
- **Recall the order of the planets in the Solar System.**

OBJECTS IN ORBIT

Planets and moons are not the only things in orbit in the <u>Solar System</u>. There are probably over a billion objects altogether, but many of them are just small lumps of rock. Here are some of the objects and some descriptions.

Activity

1 In pairs, match each object to the correct description.

<u>asteroid</u>	the star at the centre of the Solar System
<u>comet</u>	one of nine large objects that orbit the Sun in the same plane
moon	a lump of rock in orbit around the Sun
planet	an icy, rocky object that goes round the Sun in a highly elliptical orbit
Sun	an object that orbits a planet

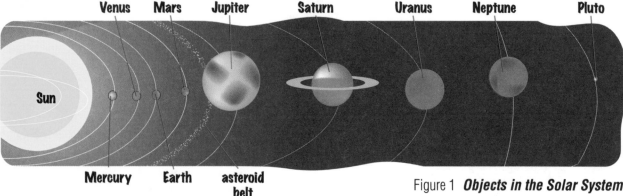

Figure 1 *Objects in the Solar System*

RELATIONSHIPS BETWEEN DATA GROUPS FOR THE PLANETS

Planet	Average distance from Sun compared to Earth	Average surface temperature in °C	Day length in Earth days	Year length in Earth years	Mass compared to Earth
Mercury	0.4	130	59	0.24	0.06
Venus	0.7	450	243	0.61	0.81
Earth	1.0	20	1	1.0	1
Mars	1.5	−50	1	1.9	0.10
Jupiter	5.2	−150	0.42	12	318
Saturn	9.5	−180	0.44	29	95
Uranus	19.2	−210	0.72	84	14
Neptune	30.0	−210	0.65	165	17
Pluto	39.5	−220	6.4	248	0.03

Activity

4 In groups of four, look at the table and discuss the statements below. Explain why you think each is correct or not. The further away a planet is from the Sun:
(a) the colder it is   **(b)** the longer its year   **(c)** the shorter its day   **(d)** the more massive it is.

STARTER

Mike Viewed EastEnders Munching Jam Sandwiches Until Nicky Phoned

This way of remembering things is called a mnemonic.
- As a class, discuss what the mnemonic represents.
- Form groups and hold a contest to see which group can invent the best mnemonic by the end of the lesson.

THE OUTER PLANETS, AND DISTANCES BETWEEN PLANETS

Activity

2 In groups of four, use books, CD-ROMs and the internet to complete the table below. Prepare an illustrated poster or leaflet on one of the outer planets. Include details about: its composition; its average temperature; its days, years and seasons; conditions on its surface.

Beyond Mars lies the **asteroid belt** where lumps of rock orbit the Sun in a ring. Further still are the **outer planets** which:
- are cooler than the inner planets
- all have moons
- are less rocky and more gaseous than the inner planets.

Planet	Average distance from Sun compared to Earth	Time taken to spin on axis in Earth days	Angle by which axis is tilted	Number of known moons
Jupiter	5.2			
Saturn	9.5			
Uranus	19.2			
Neptune	30.0			
Pluto	39.5			

Tables in this and the next panel give distances of the planets from the Sun.
- The orbit of the outermost planet, Pluto, is forty times as far away from the Sun as Earth's orbit.
- Compared to Earth's orbit (1.0), the orbit of the innermost planet, Mercury, is less than a half the distance (0.4) from the Sun.

WS 52

Activity

3 In pairs, imagine a scale drawing of the orbits of all the Solar System planets. The Earth is 1.0 m from the Sun. How far away is: **(a)** Mercury, **(b)** Pluto? Imagine all the planets on an A3 sheet of paper. Pluto is 0.40 m (40 cm) from the Sun. On this scale, how far is: **(c)** the Earth, **(d)** Mercury?

REVIEW

5 Present groups' mnemonics for remembering the order of the planets, and choose the best.

6 As a class, test the relationships in Activity 4 by: either drawing graphs of each variable against average distance from the Sun, or entering the data on a spreadsheet and using the graphing facility of the spreadsheet programme to draw graphs. Write a brief conclusion that states:
- what the graphs show
- how conclusively they show this
- whether this is what you expected to find.
  Summarise the findings on the board.

7 Explain why it is difficult to draw a scale model of the planetary orbits on a single sheet of paper.

8 Write an illustrated account of the different types of object in the Solar System.

BEYOND THE SOLAR SYSTEM

AIMS

By the end of this section you should be able to:
- **Describe the apparent movement of stars in the sky.**
- **Summarise the conditions necessary for life on other planets.**

THE SEARCH FOR LIFE ELSEWHERE

Life on Earth probably began by chance. Conditions just happened to be right. Although no evidence has been found for life elsewhere in the Solar System, conditions may once have been just right on Mars.

Primitive life does not need oxygen or sunlight. All it needs is a handful of elements and the essential ingredient, water.

Beyond the Solar System are an uncountable number of stars. Astronomers believe that some of these stars must have planets where conditions are similar to those on Earth and where life might be found.

Activity

3 In groups of four, research: either: How astronomers have looked for evidence of life on Mars, and are still looking, or: How astronomers try to detect evidence of life on planets in other solar systems. Present your findings as a report or poster. Prepare a short talk to give to the class.

A SPACE CAPSULE

Each of the Pioneer space probes carried information about Earth, for any intelligent beings that might discover the probes in space. One form of information was the plaque in Figure 2.

⊙⊙ *Links to other key ideas*

Think about the links with Adapation (page 40). You will also extend work on this topic in Year 9.

Figure 2 **The gold plaque carried by Pioneer 10, launched in 1972**

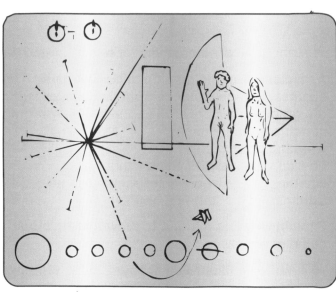

Activity

4 As a class, discuss what the objects on the plaque represent. List items that could be included in a capsule to inform other beings about planet Earth, and how it can be contacted. Choose the ten most essential items, saying why each one should be included.

STARTER

As a class, discuss the possibility of finding life:
- in the Solar System
- beyond the Solar System.

LOOKING AT THE STARS

On a clear night, you can see very many bright objects in the sky. The number is so large that there are too many to count. Some objects are stars, and some are planets in our Solar System, reflecting light from the Sun. When you look through a telescope, some of the bright objects you see are moons of planets in the Solar System. Stars and planets appear to move in different ways:

- Polaris, the Pole Star, is the one star that does not appear to move in the sky of the northern hemisphere.
- Because the Earth spins, each night the other stars seem to revolve anticlockwise around Polaris.
- Planets appear to us to have different patterns of movement. The pattern for each planet depends on its distance from the Sun.

When William Herschel first saw Uranus through his homemade telescope, he thought that he had discovered a comet.

Activity

1 Recall the differences between moons, planets and stars.

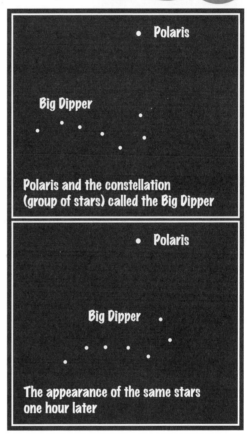

Polaris and the constellation (group of stars) called the Big Dipper

The appearance of the same stars one hour later

Figure 1 **Apparent movement of the stars**

Activity

2 In pairs, answer these questions using books, CD-ROMs and the internet.
(a) How did Herschel know that what he saw was not a star?
(b) How did he tell other astronomers about his discovery?
(c) What evidence made other astronomers think that Herschel had discovered a planet, not a comet?

REVIEW

5 Make group reports to the class of findings about the search for life elsewhere in the Solar System or beyond.

6 In groups, prepare a 5-question quick-fire quiz on one of these topics:
- days, months and years
- seeing into space
- seasons and the inner planets
- the Solar System.

In turn, each group quizzes the rest of the class.

Follow the mouse
www.seti.org/game/

7 You are to give the opening speech in a debate about life on other planets. Prepare a 10-minute talk to argue either in favour of life existing elsewhere or against life being anywhere else.

QUESTIONS AND ANSWERS

AIMS
When you read a question paper, you need to:
- Know what the questions are asking you to do.
- Use the number of marks on questions to help guide your answers.

STARTER

Work in pairs to talk about:

As a class, make a list on the board of different ways of learning for a test. What are the reasons for not doing well?

I learn for a test by...

I lose marks in tests because...

SCIENCE QUESTIONS

This is Joe's science test and what he wrote in it.

1 A balloon is filled with helium.
   a) How does the density of helium compare to air?
      Tick the correct box:

      Helium is more dense than air. ☐ *don't know*

      Helium is less dense than air   ☐ *don't know*

      Helium has the same density as air ☐ *don't know* **(1 mark)**

   b) What state is helium? *It's a gas because the balloon is floating about.* ....**(1 mark)**

   c) Explain how the particles in the balloon are arranged and how they move.
      far apart
      .... **(2 marks)**

   d) Explain why the balloon can be squashed.
      the particles can get closer together
      .... **(2 marks)**

This is the teacher's mark scheme
1 a) less dense (1)
   b) gas (1)
   c) particles are far apart (1);
      they move about quickly (1)
   d) there is a lot of space between
      particles (1); they can be pushed
      closer together (1)

Activity
2 (a) Decide how many marks Joe will get.
  (b) What advice would you give Joe to show him how to get more marks?

LOOKING AT QUESTIONS

There are four main types of questions:

Type of question	Examples
Choose an answer **Which?**	Choose... Put a tick in the box... True or false... Use these words to complete...
Short answer **One word or phrase.**	Which...? What...? Give an example of...

Type of question	Examples
Longer answer **At least one sentence.**	Explain what... Explain how... How...? What happens when...?
Reasoning and explaining **Because...**	Explain why...? Why...? Give reasons...

LOOKING AT ANSWERS

Look at these examples of questions and answers:

Q *What* did you do on Saturday morning?
....**(1 mark)**

A word or phrase is enough. **One example is enough.**

A I went shopping. ✔

Q *Explain what* you did on Saturday morning. ....**(2 marks)**

Write at least one sentence. **You need to make two clear points.**

A I went by bus to the sports shop. ✔ I bought some new trainers. ✔

Q *Explain why* you did this. ....**(2 marks)**

You need to use the word 'because' in your answer. **Give two reasons.**

A I bought some trainers because I am in the school running club ✔ and my old ones have split. ✔

Look at each other's answers to Activity 1. Discuss how you decided how much detail you needed to write. Do you think you would get 5 marks?

TIPS FOR ANSWERING QUESTIONS
● *Put your pen down* while you read the question carefully.
● Look at the *number of marks* – this is a good guide to how much detail you have to give.
● *Never leave gaps* – you do not lose marks by guessing!

Activity
1 Work in pairs. Write down answers to these questions.
• Explain how you play music at home. .... **(2 marks)**
• Who is your favourite singer or group? .... **(1 mark)**
• Explain why you like them. .... **(2 marks)**

REVIEW

3 As a group, make a spider diagram to show how to get more marks when you are answering questions.

BIOLOGY TEST QUESTIONS

1 What are the names of the parts labelled **(A)**, **(B)** and **(C)** on the diagram?

A ....

B ....

C ....**(3 marks)**

2 Use the key to classify these organisms:

> **Key**
> 1 Has no wings ....= **spider**
>   Has wings ....Go to 2
> 2 Wings are folded across the back ....= **beetle**
>   Has outstretched wings ....Go to 3
> 3 Has 1 pair of wings ....= **hoverfly**
>   Has 2 pairs of wings ....Go to 4
> 4 Has an elongated abdomen ....= **dragonfly**
>   Abdomen has warning stripes ....= **wasp**

(5 marks)

3 Use the food chain to answer the questions.

a) Which one is the producer? ....**(1 mark)**

b) Which one is the predator? ....**(1 mark)**

c) In which direction should the arrows go to represent the flow of energy?

....**(1 mark)**

4 **a)** Which part of the female reproductive system stores the eggs?

....**(1 mark)**

b) Where does the fetus develop? ....**(1 mark)**

c) What is the function of the placenta? ....

....**(3 marks)**

5 Name 3 characteristics that are specific to mammals.

....

....

....**(3 marks)**

6 Give 3 different physical factors in the environments of these 2 habitats.

....
....
....**(3 marks)**

7 Put these 3 terms in the correct order to show what happens during reproduction:

fertilisation   implantation   ovulation

....**(3 marks)**

8 Name 3 parts that both cells have, and 3 that only plant cells have.

....
....**(6 marks)**

9 Explain how these cells are adapted to their function.

....
....**(2 marks)**

10 a) Sort these characteristics into those controlled by the genes inherited from parents and those controlled by the environment:
    • eye colour   • accent   • tongue rolling   • height   • favourite food

....
....**(5 marks)**

b) Which of the characteristics above would show continuous variation in the population?

....**(1 mark)**

c) Which graph shape represents continuous variation?

....**(1 mark)**

CHEMISTRY TEST QUESTIONS

11 Harry dissolves some copper sulphate crystals in water.

1 g of copper sulphate crystals

spatula

beaker

20 g of water   copper sulphate solution

a) Copy and complete the table.

Name of **solvent**	....
Name of **solute**	....
Mass of copper sulphate solution	.... g

(3 marks)

b) How can Harry tell when all the copper sulphate has dissolved?

....(1 mark)

c) How could Harry make the copper sulphate dissolve more quickly?

....(1 mark)

d) Explain how Harry could get the copper sulphate crystals back from the solution.

....

....(2 marks)

12 Use these diagrams to answer the questions below.

A   B   C

Which box, **A**, **B** or **C**, shows the arrangement of particles in:

a) helium gas ....(1 mark)

b) water ....(1 mark)

c) copper metal ....(1 mark)

d) Explain why copper has a fixed shaped but water can be poured.

....

....(2 marks)

13 Look at these examples of changes.

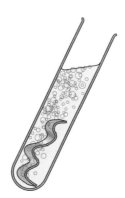

a) Which changes are irreversible?

....

....(2 marks)

b) Which changes show gases being made?

....

....(2 marks)

c) Explain how you could reverse the melting of an ice cube.

....

....(2 marks)

d) Copy the following and fill in the blanks. **(3 marks)**

When water evaporates it turns to .... When evaporation is reversed it is

called .... No new products are made during a .... change.

14 a) Copy the boxes and draw lines to connect the reactants with the correct products.

Reactants	Products
magnesium + oxygen	carbon dioxide + water
methane + oxygen	magnesium oxide
magnesium and hydrochloric acid	calcium chloride + carbon dioxide + water
calcium carbonate and hydrochloric acid	hydrogen + magnesium chloride

(3 marks)

b) Which reactant in **a)** turns universal indicator red? ....(1 mark)

15 The diagram shows a spring attached to a stand.

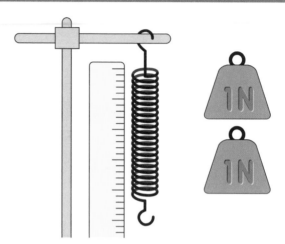

a) What will happen when a 1 N weight is added to the end of the spring?

....**(1 mark)**

b) What will happen when a second 1 N weight is added to the spring?

....**(1 mark)**

c) What will happen when the weights are removed?

....

....**(2 marks)**

16 The cartoon shows a tug of war.

a) What will happen if the two teams are pulling with the same force?

....**(1 mark)**

b) What will happen if the team on the left pulls with a greater force?

....**(1 mark)**

c) What force stops the feet of the people from slipping on the ground?

....**(1 mark)**

d) Why do people in tug of war teams wear shoes with rough soles?

....**(1 mark)**

17 Natural gas is used to heat homes.

a) What type of energy is stored in natural gas?

....**(1 mark)**

b) What two types of energy are given out when natural gas burns in a gas fire?

....

....**(2 marks)**

c) Natural gas is a 'non-renewable' source of energy. Explain what 'non-renewable' means.

....**(1 mark)**

d) Give two examples of renewable energy sources.

....

....**(2 marks)**

18 a) Copy the names and symbols below and draw lines to connect the name of the circuit component to the correct symbol. **(4 marks)**

Name   bulb   cell   open switch   battery   buzzer

Symbol

b) Which of the following circuits will contain the brightest bulb or bulbs?

  A   **B**   **C**   **D**

....**(1 mark)**

19 a) What season is it in the northern parts of the Earth when it is autumn in the southern parts?

....**(1 mark)**

b) Give two differences between summer and winter days.

....

....**(2 marks)**

USEFUL FORMULAE AND TABLES

BIOLOGY

CHARACTERISTICS OF LIFE

MRS GREN = Movement, Respiration, Sensitivity, Growth, Reproduction, Excretion, Nutrition.

STRUCTURE OF LIVING THINGS

Cells → Tissues → Organs → Systems → Organism

FOOD CHAINS

Producer → Primary consumer → Secondary consumer

CONTINUOUS AND DISCONTINUOUS DATA

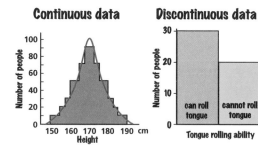

Continuous data

Discontinuous data

TAXONOMY

Organism (living thing)

Animal Kingdom — Plant Kingdom

Invertebrates (without a backbone) — Vertebrates (with a backbone)

Fish　Amphibians　Reptiles　Birds　Mammals

Examples:

CHEMISTRY

SOLIDS, LIQUIDS AND GASES

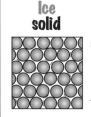

Ice solid		Water liquid		Steam gas
	melting → ← freezing		evaporating → ← condensing	

REACTIONS OF ACIDS

- When **acids** react with some **metals**, **hydrogen** gas is made.
- **Hydrogen** makes a lighted splint go 'pop'.
- When **acids** react with **carbonates**, **carbon dioxide** gas is made.
- **Carbon dioxide** turns **lime water** cloudy.

PHYSICS

CIRCUIT SYMBOLS

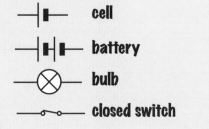

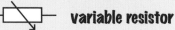

- cell
- battery
- bulb
- closed switch
- open switch
- buzzer
- fixed resistor
- variable resistor

FORMS OF ENERGY

- Heat energy
- Light energy
- Movement energy (sometimes called 'kinetic')
- Electrical energy
- Chemical energy
- Sound energy

THE PERIODIC TABLE

Key

atomic mass
symbol
name
atomic number

■ metals
□ non-metals

— transition metals

I	II											III	IV	V	VI	VII	0
1 H Hydrogen 1																	**4** He Helium 2
7 Li Lithium 3	**9** Be Beryllium 4											**11** B Boron 5	**12** C Carbon 6	**14** N Nitrogen 7	**16** O Oxygen 8	**19** F Fluorine 9	**20** Ne Neon 10
23 Na Sodium 11	**24** Mg Magnesium 12											**27** Al Aluminium 13	**28** Si Silicon 14	**31** P Phosphorus 15	**32** S Sulphur 16	**35.5** Cl Chlorine 17	**40** Ar Argon 18
39 K Potassium 19	**40** Ca Calcium 20	**45** Sc Scandium 21	**48** Ti Titanium 22	**51** V Vanadium 23	**52** Cr Chromium 24	**55** Mn Manganese 25	**56** Fe Iron 26	**59** Co Cobalt 27	**59** Ni Nickel 28	**64** Cu Copper 29	**65** Zn Zinc 30	**70** Ga Gallium 31	**73** Ge Germanium 32	**75** As Arsenic 33	**79** Se Selenium 34	**80** Br Bromine 35	**84** Kr Krypton 36
85.5 Rb Rubidium 37	**88** Sr Strontium 38	**89** Y Yttrium 39	**91** Zr Zirconium 40	**93** Nb Niobium 41	**96** Mo Molybdenum 42	**99** Tc Technetium 43	**101** Ru Ruthenium 44	**103** Rh Rhodium 45	**106** Pd Palladium 46	**108** Ag Silver 47	**112** Cd Cadmium 48	**115** In Indium 49	**119** Sn Tin 50	**122** Sb Antimony 51	**128** Te Tellurium 52	**127** I Iodine 53	**131** Xe Xenon 54
133 Cs Caesium 55	**137** Ba Barium 56	**139** La Lanthanum 57	**178.5** Hf Hafnium 72	**181** Ta Tantalum 73	**184** W Tungsten 74	**186** Re Rhenium 75	**190** Os Osmium 76	**192** Ir Iridium 77	**195** Pt Platinum 78	**197** Au Gold 79	**201** Hg Mercury 80	**204** Tl Thallium 81	**207** Pb Lead 82	**209** Bi Bismuth 83	**210** Po Polonium 84	**210** At Astatine 85	**222** Rn Radon 86
223 Fr Francium 87	**226** Ra Radium 88	**227** Ac Actinium 89	– Db Dubnium 104	– Jl Joliotium 105	– Rf Rutherfordium 106	– Bh Bohrium 107	– Hn Hahnium 108	– Mt Meitnerium 109									

INDEX AND GLOSSARY

INDEX AND GLOSSARY

143

Published by Letts Educational
The Chiswick Centre
414 Chiswick High Road
London W4 5TF
Telephone: 020 8996 3333
Fax: 020 8742 8390
E-mail: mail@lettsed.co.uk
Website: www.letts-education.com

Letts Educational is part of the Granada Learning Group.
Granada Learning is a division of Granada plc.

British Library Cataloguing in Publication Data
A catalogue record for this book is available from the British Library.

Acknowledgements
Every effort has been made to contact the holders of copyright material, but if any have been inadvertently overlooked the publishers will be pleased to make the necessary arrangements at the first opportunity.

The publishers would like to thank the following for permission to reproduce photographs, (T = Top, B = Bottom, C = Centre, L= Left, R = Right):

Ardea London/M Clay, page 51CR; Martyn Chillmaid, pages 82BR, 91, 93TL; Leslie Garland Photo Library/M Fuller, page 80TR; Sally and Richard Greenhill Photo Library, page 37; Robert Harding Picture Library/S Grandadam, page 82BL; Graeme Morris, page 80C; NHPA/H Ausloos, page 42TC, T Kitchin & V Hurst, page 42BR&TL, ANT Photo Library, page 42BC, N J Dennis, page 51BR; Nature Picture Library/A Harrington, page 42BL, D Watts, page 42TR, D McEwan, page 51BL; Science Photo Library/M W Tweedie, page 13, Dr G Gaugler, page 20L, Dr J Burgess, page 26, NASA, pages 68BR, 122, Rosenfeld Images Ltd, page 68BL; SHOUT Pictures, pages 82BC, 107; Still Pictures/D Garcia, page 93TR; Tony Waltham/Geophotos, page 80TL.

This book was designed and produced for Letts Educational by Ken Vail Graphic Design, Cambridge

Commissioned by Helen Clark

Project management by Vicky Butt

Edited by Pat Winter

Illustrations by Phil Burrows

Production by PDQ

Printed and bound in Scotland by Scotprint, Haddington

With thanks to John Watts

Contents key
Objectives are numbered consecutively as laid out in the *Framework for Teaching Science* pages 25–30.

C = Cells	I = Interdependence
P = Particles	E = Energy
F = Forces	SE = Scientific enquiry
